USING YOUR METER

METER

VOM and DVM Multitesters

By
Alvis J. Evans

Radio Shack®

A DIVISION OF TANDY CORPORATION
FT. WORTH, TEXAS 76102

D0316895

This book was developed and published by:
Master Publishing, Inc.
Richardson, Texas

Design and artwork by:
Plunk Design
Dallas, Texas

Printing by:
Arby Graphic Service, Inc.
Chicago, Illinois

9   8

TABLE OF CONTENTS

PREFACE

Making basic electrical circuit measurements of voltage, current, or resistance with a meter helps significantly in understanding an electrical circuit to tell if it is operating properly or if repair or maintenance is necessary to correct its operation.

This book has been written to help you understand how meters work and how to use them to make basic electrical measurements. It very much emphasizes "how to do" the various measurements. In addition, it provides understanding of basic concepts and fundamentals, so that you have more appreciation of what is actually happening in the electrical circuit being measured. It is fully illustrated to visually enhance the understanding.

The book begins by explaining the basic concepts of a VOM and DVM, relating how the analog and digital meters differ, and the advantages and disadvantages of each. Following a discussion about multitester measurements, where polarity, reference point, meter loading, are the topics, basic dc and ac measurements are discussed with actual step-by-step procedures defined for voltage, current, and resistance measurements. These principles are then applied to measuring individual components — resistors, capacitors, inductors, semiconductor devices — individually and in circuits. The book concludes with numerous electrical measurements on common systems around the home. Power distribution, lighting, heating and air conditioning, appliances, smoke alarms, cassette recorders/players and automotive circuits are included. After reading this book and following its suggested procedures, you should be able to make circuit measurements and detect improper circuit operation. We wish you success — the rest is up to you.

AJE
MP

VOM—
THE BASIC CONCEPTS

INTRODUCTION

Electricity seems so elusive, so mysterious. We know it is used to operate most of the equipment around the home and the office. Home lighting, appliances, heating and air conditioning, televisions, stereos, workshop tools, video games and home computers depend upon electricity for their operation. Although we can see and feel the effects of electricity, it would benefit one a great deal to understand the effects if one could measure it. That is the purpose of meters — voltmeters, ammeters and ohmmeters. They measure basic electrical quantities such as voltage, current and resistance.

This book has been written to help you understand how such meters work and how they can be used to make basic electrical measurements — in the home, in the workshop, at the office, on the job.

There are two basic types of meters used to make electrical measurements. One type has a needle that deflects along a scale and indicates the value of a quantity by the position of the needle on the scale. This is an analog meter, and is commonly called a voltmeter, ammeter, ohmmeter, VOM, multimeter or multitester depending on the quantities that it measures. The meter mechanism is generally of the D'Arsonal type which will be detailed later.

Figure 1-1 shows a typical analog meter. The main meter parts are the meter movement (behind the scales) that contains the needle that deflects to the right along a scale, the switches that select which quantity the meter is set to measure and the full-scale range of the meter for the measurement, and several adjusting controls and jacks that accept plug-in test leads used to connect the meter to a component or circuit for measurement.

The other type is a digital meter. Any quantity that is measured appears as a number on a digital display. It is commonly called a digital voltmeter, DVM, digital multimeter or digital multitester.

Figure 1-1. Analog Meter

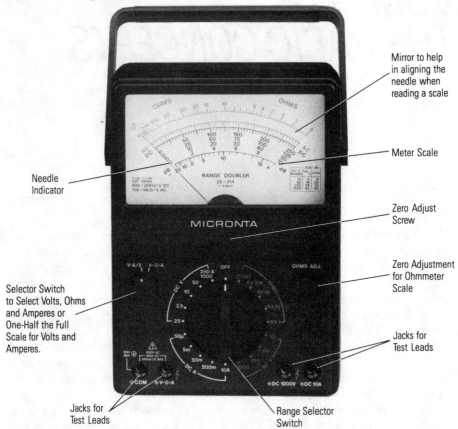

Mirror to help in aligning the needle when reading a scale

Meter Scale

Needle Indicator

Zero Adjust Screw

MICRONTA

Zero Adjustment for Ohmmeter Scale

Selector Switch to Select Volts, Ohms and Amperes or One-Half the Full Scale for Volts and Amperes.

Jacks for Test Leads

Jacks for Test Leads

Range Selector Switch

A typical digital meter is shown in *Figure 1-2*. The digital display is the main meter output, indicating the numerical value of the measurement. A selector switch selects the type measurement. The full-scale range of the measurement is selected automatically. Jacks accept the plug-in test leads, and the ON-OFF switch applies battery power to the internal circuits when in the ON position. A set of test leads is shown in *Figure 1-3*.

Let's look at the most common type meter first — the analog VOM (Volt-Ohm Milliammeter).

THE BASIC METER MOVEMENT

The VOM, with its needle that moves on a scale, is basically a small electrical motor. To understand electrical motor action it is necessary to understand two very simple electrical principles: 1. What happens when there is current in a wire or other type conductor of electricity, and 2. magnetism and magnetic fields. Let's take magnetism first.

Figure 1-2. Digital Meter

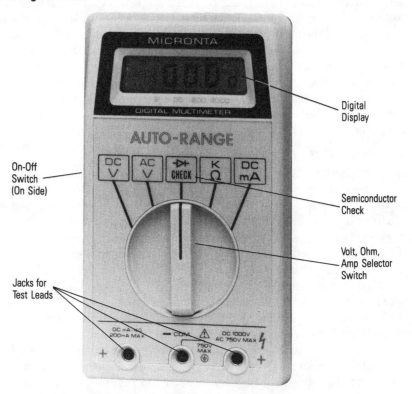

Digital
Display

On-Off
Switch
(On Side)

Semiconductor
Check

Volt, Ohm,
Amp Selector
Switch

Jacks for
Test Leads

Figure 1-3. Test Leads

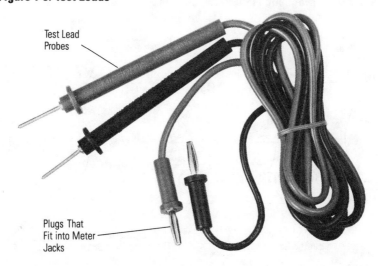

Test Lead
Probes

Plugs That
Fit into Meter
Jacks

Figure 1-4 shows a coil of wire with many turns mounted on a pivot between the north and south poles of a magnet. There is a magnetic field running from the north pole to the south pole. The field is invisible, but if it were visible, it would appear as lines starting at the north pole and stopping at the south pole, as shown in *Figure 1-4*. The field lines leave and enter the magnet's surface perpendicular (at right angles) to the surface. The pole pieces have a special shape so that the magnetic field is very uniform throughout the air gap between the pole pieces and the meter movement coil. The purpose of such a uniform field between pole pieces will not be apparent until we look at the second simple principle of motor action — current in a wire or conductor.

Current in a Wire

A Danish physicist, Hans Christian Oersted, in 1819, discovered that a magnetic field surrounds a wire or conductor in which there is current. The effect is shown in *Figure 1-5*. A current in the wire in the direction shown will produce a magnetic field counter-clockwise around the wire as shown — the larger the current, the larger the magnetic field. In this book those of you that are familiar with electron current use the dotted line directions for current, and those familiar with conventional current use the solid line directions.

Figure 1-6 is a cross section through the pole pieces and one loop of the coil of wire shown in *Figure 1-4*. It shows the motor action. As an example, let's look at leg A of the loop of wire in *Figure 1-6*. Electron current is out of the page; therefore, the magnetic field produced is clockwise around the wire. At the top of leg A, the current magnetic field adds to the uniform magnetic field; at the bottom of the leg A it subtracts. As a result, a force is developed that pushes on the loop of wire and causes it to rotate. The stronger magnetic field at the top forces the leg A of the loop down.

Figure 1-4. Meter Coil in Magnetic Field Between Pole Pieces of Magnet

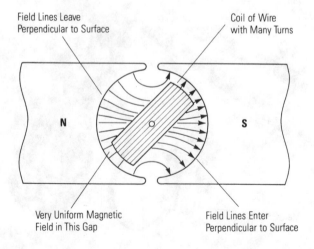

Field Lines Leave Perpendicular to Surface

Coil of Wire with Many Turns

N   S

Very Uniform Magnetic Field in This Gap

Field Lines Enter Perpendicular to Surface

Figure 1-5. Magnetic Field Around a Wire Carrying Current

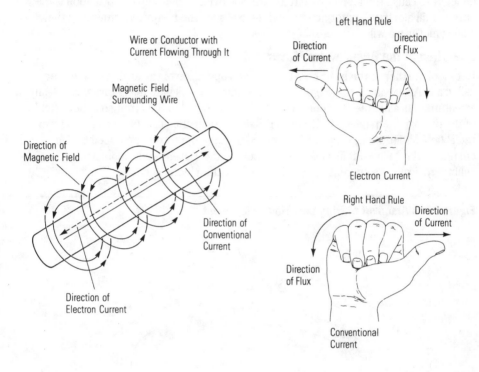

Wire or Conductor with Current Flowing Through It

Magnetic Field Surrounding Wire

Direction of Magnetic Field

Direction of Conventional Current

Direction of Electron Current

Left Hand Rule

Direction of Current

Direction of Flux

Electron Current

Right Hand Rule

Direction of Current

Direction of Flux

Conventional Current

Figure 1-6. Motor Action — Wire Carrying Current in a Magnetic Field

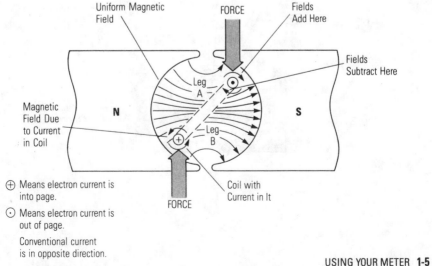

Uniform Magnetic Field

FORCE

Fields Add Here

Fields Subtract Here

Magnetic Field Due to Current in Coil

N

S

Leg A

Leg B

Coil with Current in It

FORCE

⊕ Means electron current is into page.

⊙ Means electron current is out of page.

Conventional current is in opposite direction.

The continuous current in the loop goes into the page in leg B. The current magnetic field now is in a direction to force leg B up as shown, thus aiding the force on leg A to cause the loop of wire to rotate clockwise. This simple explanation is the basis for all electrical motor action, and the basis for the meter movements of the analog meter we will be discussing.

Operation of the Basic Meter Movement

Let's look further at the basic construction and operation of the analog type meter called a D'Arsonval meter (*Figure 1-7*). The movable coil with many turns, called an armature, has a needle attached to it, and is located within the strong magnetic field of the permanent magnet (PM) which is hidden under the scale plate . The uniform radial field about the moving coil is required to make the torque produced by the current in the coil result in a linear movement of the meter needle along the calibrated scale. As current increases, the deflection increases.

Figure 1-7. D'Arsonval Moving Coil Meter Movement

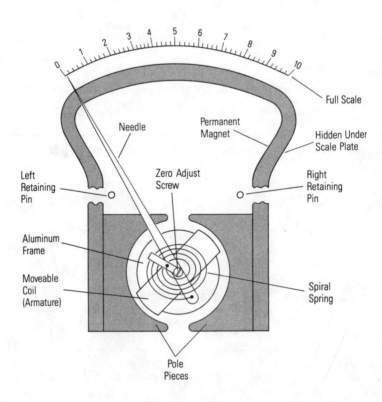

One end of the needle is attached to a spiral spring so the needle will be returned to an initial position when the current in the coil is removed. The springs are calibrated and the coil and needle are balanced so that the total assembly produces a linear deflection on the meter scale as the current in the coil is increased linearly.

The other end of the spiral spring is attached to a ZERO ADJUST screw located on the core of the moving coil. With the ZERO ADJUST, the initial static position of the meter movement is adjusted mechanically to zero on the scale by varying the position of the end of the spiral spring. Care must be taken in making this adjustment because of the delicate construction of the spiral spring.

The complete needle assembly usually is constructed around an aluminum frame so that the assembly is very sturdy. The aluminum frame also serves a purpose for damping, which will be discussed a bit later.

Since the radial magnetic field is produced by a permanent magnet, the direction of the force of this field is always in one direction. Thus, the current must pass through the coil in one direction only to cause an upscale deflection on the needle. If current passes through the meter movement coil in the other direction, the needle deflects backwards against the meter's left retaining pin. This is one of the most common ways of damaging or burning out a meter — *passing too much current through the coil in the wrong direction.*

Damping

To prevent overshoot when the meter coil and needle assembly moves, it must be damped. As mentioned, the aluminum frame accomplishes the damping. It is effectively a short circuited single turn loop within the meter's magnetic field. A loop of wire moving in a magnetic field will have a voltage induced in the loop. Any movement of the meter armature moves the frame, and the induced voltage causes a current in the frame. As with any current in a conductor, the frame current develops a magnetic field which interacts with the strong magnetic field of the permanent magnet and offers a slight opposition to the movement of the coil. This method of damping the moving coil movement is an application of a law developed by Heinrich Lenz, a German physicist. The law states that the resultant current in a wire moving in a magnetic field produces a magnetic field that opposes the original magnetic field that generates the voltage that produced the current.

BASIC CHARACTERISTICS

Meter Movement Sensitivity

The sensitivity of the meter movement depends upon the current required for full scale deflection. It varies inversely with the current; that is, the most sensitive meter requires the least current for full-scale deflection. The amount of current required to deflect the needle full scale depends upon the number of turns of wire on the moving coil. When more turns are added, usually by using smaller and smaller wire, a stonger magnetic field is created to react with the permanent magnetic field. Smaller wire also keeps the mass of the meter movement low.

● Measuring Sensitivity

The sensitivity of a meter can be determined by measuring the current required to produce full-scale deflection. To do this, a standard current meter is placed in series with the unknown meter and a source of current applied to the meter as shown in *Figure 1-8*. Since the current is the same in all parts of a series circuit, the amount of current to produce full-scale deflection on the unknown meter can be read directly from the standard meter. Meter sensitivities range from a few microamperes for very sensitive movements to 50 to 1,000 microamperes for average movements used for multitesters that measure voltage, current and resistance.

Internal Resistance

The meter sensitivity and the internal dc resistance of a meter movement are fixed by the design; definite characteristics that cannot be altered unless the physical construction of the meter movement is changed. To measure a meter's internal resistance, with the full-scale current through a meter indicated by the standard current meter, a voltmeter is connected across the unknown meter to measure the voltage drop across its internal resistance. The meter's internal resistance may then be obtained by Ohm's law:

$$R_M = \frac{V_M}{I_M}$$

Figure 1-8. Measuring a Meter's Sensitivity and Internal Resistance

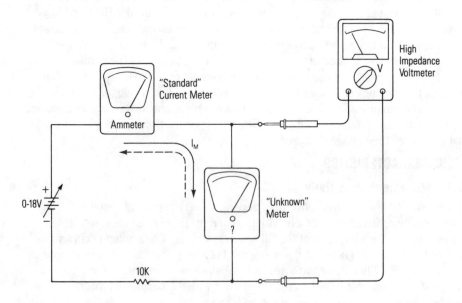

where V_M is the voltage across the meter and I_M is the current through it for a full-scale reading. A meter that is designed to have full-scale deflection with a very low current will have high sensitivity and high internal resistance.

CAUTION: A sensitive meter movement can be easily destroyed by connecting an ohmmeter across it in an attempt to measure its internal resistance. The ohmmeter has an internal battery and can supply current. The current from the ohmmeter may be 100 times that required to deflect the meter full scale.

Meter Accuracy

There are many factors that affect a meter's accuracy: the design of the meter, the quality of its parts, the care in its manufacture, the accuracy of its calibration, the environment it is used in, and the care it has had since being put into service.

The accuracy of a meter that is used in everyday applications (not under controlled environmental conditions) is usually between 0.01% and 3%. The accuracy of meters that have D'Arsonval movements (*Figure 1-7*) that are commonly used in all types of measuring instruments is about 1% of the full-scale reading. If a voltmeter has a 10 volt scale and it has a 1% accuracy, any reading is going to be accurate to ± 0.1 volt. The stated accuracy of the meter in percent refers to the percent of full-scale reading on any range.

Let's look at *Figure 1-9*. The accuracy of a voltage reading for a meter that has a stated accuracy of 1% is plotted against the voltage to be read for three full-scale ranges — 10 volt, 5 volt, and 2.5 volt. If a voltage of 2 volts is measured, it will be accurate to $\pm 0.1V$ (5%) if measured on the 10 volt range, $\pm 0.05V$ (2.5%) if measured on the 5 volt range, and $\pm 0.025V$ (1.25%) if measured on the 2.5 volt range.

As a result, a meter reading taken at the low end of the scale is going to have a greater percent of absolute error than a reading near full scale. Thus, to have the greatest accuracy, it is best when making measurements to chose the range for the meter so that the deflection is nearest to full scale. The closer the reading of the meter to full scale, the less the absolute error.

AMMETERS

The simplest ammeter contains only the basic meter movement. It can measure values of current up to its sensitivity rating (full-scale deflection). Meter movements that require a large current for full-scale deflection are not practical because of the large wire they would require on the coil, and thus, the large mass. Therefore, highly sensitive meter movements are desensitized by placing low value resistors called "shunts" in parallel with the meter movement to extend their current handling range. If a meter movement requires 100 microamperes for full-scale deflection and the meter is to have a 10 milliampere (10,000 microamperes) scale, a shunt across the meter must have a resistance value to carry 9900 microamperes.

Figure 1-9. Accuracy Range of 1% Meter on Various Full-Scale Ranges

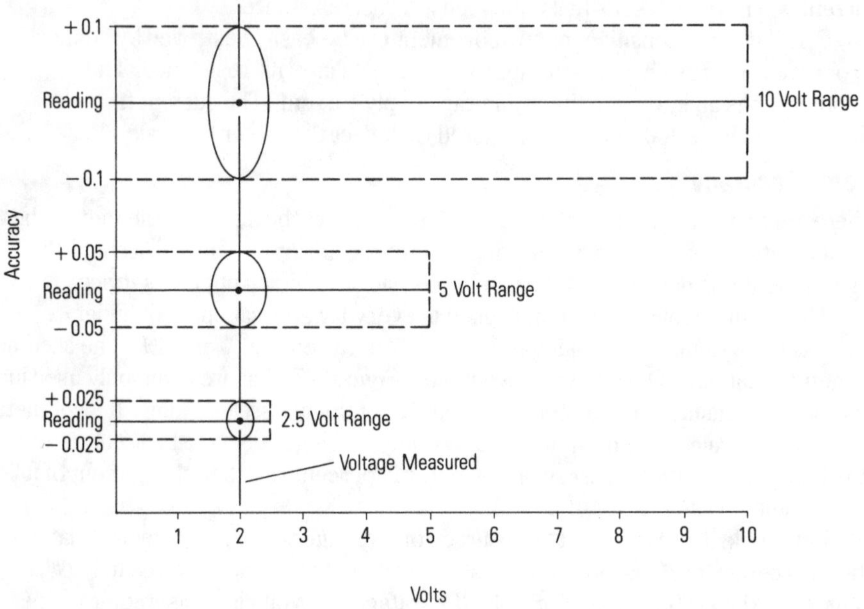

Simple Ammeters

Figure 1-10 shows a single shunt across a basic meter movement to extend the range of the movement. Shunts are easily calculated by applying Ohm's Law (V = IR) and the principles of a parallel circuit, if the meter movement's internal resistance R_M is known. The derivation of the equation for the ammeter shunt resistor R_S is as follows:

The voltage across the shunt, V_S, is equal to the voltage across the meter V_M. Therefore,

$$V_S = V_M$$

V_S is equal to the current through the shunt, I_S, times the shunt resistance, R_S. V_M is equal to the current through the meter movement, I_M, times the meter resistance, R_M. Therefore,

$$I_S \times R_S = I_M \times R_M$$

Solving for R_S gives,

$$R_S = \frac{(I_M \times R_M)}{I_S}$$

Substituting $I_T - I_M$ for I_S gives,

$$R_S = \frac{(I_M \times R_M)}{(I_T - I_M)}$$

Figure 1-10. Using a Single Shunt to Extend the Range of a Basic Meter Movement

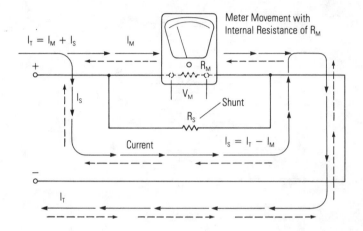

The use of this meter shunt equation will provide the correct value of resistance to be added in parallel with the meter movement to increase the current handling capability of the meter.

Example: If $I_M = 1$ milliampere, $R_M = 1000$ ohms and I_T is to be a full-scale range of 1 ampere, then the shunt resistance is:

$$R_S = \frac{0.001A \times 1000 \text{ ohms}}{(1,000-1) \text{ mA}}$$

$$R_S = \frac{1V}{999mA}$$

$$R_S = \frac{1}{0.999A}$$

$$R_S = 1.001 \text{ ohms}$$

Multirange Ammeters

● Simple Shunts

What we have said is that a basic meter movement has a given sensitivity — a given amount of current must pass through it to produce full-scale deflection. By using suitable shunts, the range of current that a given movement can measure is increased. This is essentially the process used in the construction of multirange ammeters. In *Figure 1-11*, a four-range ammeter is shown. The meter leads are used to connect the meter in the circuit to measure a current. Note the lowest range (position 1) uses the meter's basic sensitivity of 1 milliampere (1 mA) with no shunt.

Figure 1-11. A Multi-Range Ammeter

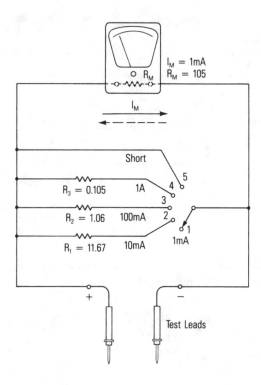

The values of the shunts are given. These values may be verified using the equation for R_s just discussed. The fifth position on the switch is marked SHORT which takes the meter out of the circuit without physically disconnecting its leads.

● Ring Shunts

Another type of shunt commonly used in multimeters or multitesters is shown in *Figure 1-12*. It is called a ring-type shunt or Ayrton "universal" shunt. In the circuit, the resistors, R_2, R_3, R_4, R_5 and R_6, are used as shunts. They are all connected in series and, in turn, are connected in parallel across R_1 and the basic meter movement. R_1 is always in series with the meter movement.

The position of the switch, S_1, determines which of the resistors R_2 through R_5 also are placed in series with the basic meter movement. The remaining resistors form the shunt to increase the current range. The resistance needed for each current range is calculated in the same way as in the simple shunt circuit, except that the resistance in series with the meter is added to R_M.

Figure 1-12. Ring Shunt

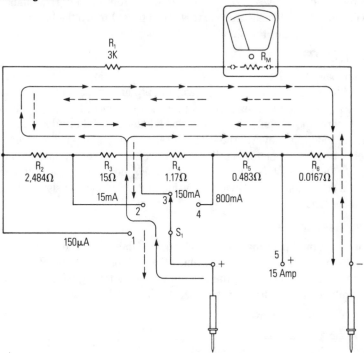

For example, S_1 in *Figure 1-12*, is in position 3, the 150 milliampere (150 mA) scale. For this full-scale value, series resistors R_4, R_5, and R_6 are in shunt with the total series resistance represented by R_1, R_2, R_3 and the internal resistance of the meter, R_M. Because of the number of unknowns in this circuit, it is impossible to use the previous equation for calculating R_S. Rather, an equation based upon Ohm's law and the laws for parallel circuits can be derived. We will not derive the equation, because of the length of the derivation, but just offer the equation for use. It is

$$R_S = \frac{(R_{sum} \times I_M)}{I_T}$$

where R_S equals the total value of the shunt, R_{sum} equals the sum of the resistances in the ring of the ring-type shunt, I_M equals the maximum current through the meter movement (its sensitivity), I_T equals the new full-scale value of the current. In *Figure 1-12*, R_{sum} would be equal to $R_1 + R_2 + R_3 + R_4 + R_5 + R_6$.

The ring type shunt eliminates the problem of high contact resistance which can cause errors in the simple shunt meters. It also eliminates the need of a special type of make-before-break type switch on the range switch of the ammeter of *Figure 1-11*.

The make-before-break switch protects the basic movement from high currents as the selector switch of *Figure 1-11* is switched to different ranges. Examining the circuit will show that full measured current could pass through the basic movement if the selector switch opens the shunt circuit on switching.

BASIC VOLTMETERS

Using Ohm's law ($V = IR$) again, where V is the voltage applied, I is the circuit current and R is the total circuit resistance, the product of the meter movement's sensitivity, I_M, and the meter movement internal resistance, R_M, equals the voltage across the meter movement, V_M, for full-scale deflection. When additional series resistance is added, it converts the basic meter movement into a direct current (dc) voltmeter. The series resistor is called a multiplier. The basic circuit is shown in *Figure 1-13*. The value of the multiplier resistor, R_X, determines the voltage range for full-scale deflection. By changing the value of the multiplier resistor, the full-scale voltage range can be changed.

Multiplier Resistance

The value of the multiplier may be found by using Ohm's Law and the rules of a series circuit. Let's look again at *Figure 1-13*. Since the multiplier resistor, R_X, is in series with the basic meter movement, the current I_M passes through R_X. If V equals the full-scale voltage of the voltmeter, then, according to Ohm's law,

$$V = I_M (R_X + R_M)$$

Figure 1-13. The Basic Circuit for a DC Voltmeter

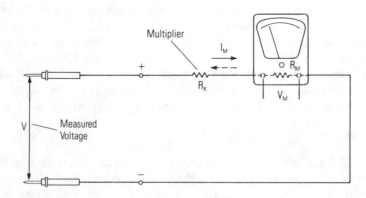

Expanding the equation gives

$$V = I_M R_X + I_M R_M$$

Rearranging,

$$V - I_M R_M = I_M R_X$$

Solving for R_X gives

$$R_X = \frac{V - I_M R_M}{I_M}$$

Which may be arranged as

$$R_X = \frac{V}{I_M} - R_M$$

Example: Let's change the basic meter movement of *Figure 1-11* into a dc voltmeter with a 10 volt full-scale range. For this example, $V = 10$ volts, $I_M = 1$ milliampere (0.001A), and $R_M = 105$ ohms. Therefore,

$$R_X = \frac{10 \text{ volts}}{0.001A} - 105 \text{ ohms}$$

$$R_X = (10,000 - 105) \text{ ohms}$$

$$R_X = 9,895 \text{ ohms}$$

When 10 volts is applied to the circuit of *Figure 1-13*, with $R_X = 9,895$ ohms and $R_M = 105$ ohms for the basic meter movement, one milliampere of current will deflect the meter to full scale.

Multirange Voltmeters

The selection of one of a number of multiplier resistors by means of a RANGE switch provides a voltmeter with a number of voltage ranges.

Figure 1-14 shows a multirange voltmeter using a four-position switch and hence four multiplier resistors. The multiplier in each range was calculated using the simple equation for R_X given previously.

A variation of the circuit of *Figure 1-14* is shown in *Figure 1-15*. In this circuit, V_4 is a higher voltage range than V_3, V_3 is higher than V_2, and V_2 is higher than V_1. As a result, the multiplier resistors of the lower ranges can be included as the multiplier for the higher range. An advantage to this circuit is that all multipliers except the first have standard resistance values which are less expensive and can be obtained commercially in precision tolerances. The first multiplier resistor R_1 is the only special resistor that must be manufactured to meet the particular requirements of the meter movement.

Figure 1-14. Simple Multirange DC Voltmeter

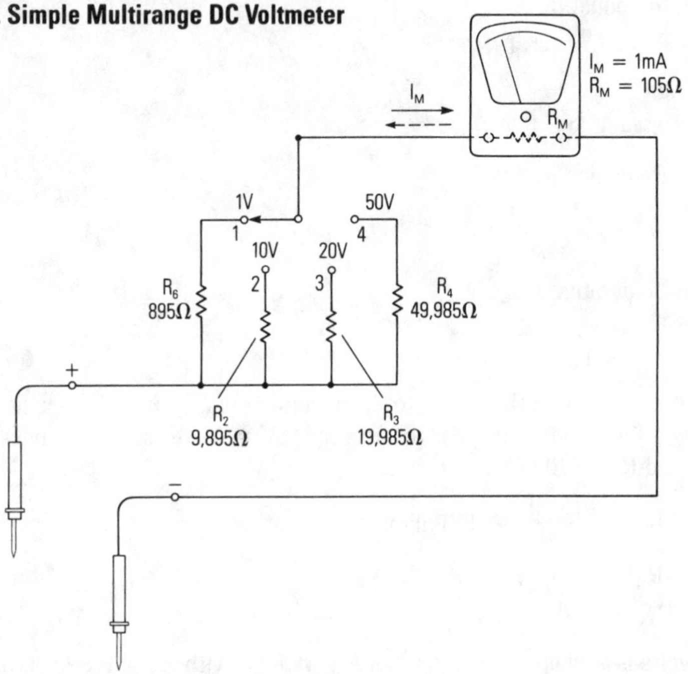

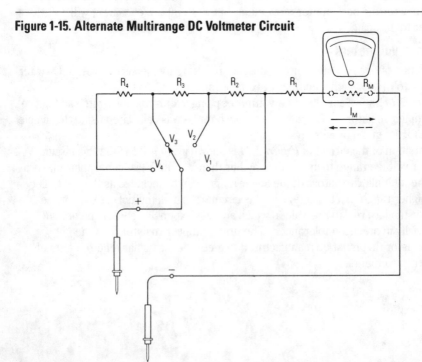

Figure 1-15. Alternate Multirange DC Voltmeter Circuit

Voltmeter Sensitivity

Figure 1-16 shows the typical way a voltmeter is used to make a voltage measurement — in this case, the voltage across resistor R_2. The voltmeter is connected across or in parallel with the circuit component (R_2) to measure the voltage. The voltmeter must have a current I_M through the meter movement to produce the deflection. This current must be supplied by the circuit and reduces the current through R_2 as shown in *Figure 1-16*. It is desirable that the resistance of the voltmeter ($R_X + R_M$) be much higher than the resistance of the device to be measured. This reduces the current drawn from the circuit by the voltmeter; and therefore, increases the accuracy of the voltage measurement.

The value of the voltmeter resistance (referred to as input resistance) depends on the sensitivity of the basic meter movement. The greater the sensitivity of the meter movement, the smaller the current required for full-scale deflection and the higher the input resistance. When expressing the sensitivity of the voltmeter, the term "ohms per volt" is used exclusively. It is referred to as the voltmeter sensitivity.

The sensitivity of the voltmeter, S, is easily calculated by taking the reciprocal of the full-scale deflection current of the basic meter movement or:

$$S = \frac{1}{I_M}$$

Example: If a meter movement with a sensitivity of 50 microamperes (0.000050A) full-scale current deflection is used to make a voltmeter, the voltmeter than has a sensitivity of:

$$S = \frac{1}{50 \times 10^{-6}} = \frac{1}{0.000050A}$$

$$S = 20,000 \text{ ohm per volt}$$

Figure 1-16. Voltage Measurement

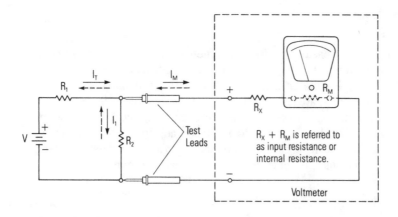

If the full-scale voltage range is set on the 1 volt range, the input resistance is 20,000 ohms; if set on the 20 volt range, the input resistance is 400,000 ohms.

BASIC OHMMETERS

Since electrical resistance is measured in ohms, a common instrument used to measure resistance is called an ohmmeter. Recall, according to Ohm's law, that the resistance, R, in a dc circuit can be determined by measuring the current, I, in a circuit as a result of applying a voltage, V. The voltage divided by the current is the resistance value, or

$$R = \frac{V}{I}$$

The resistance will be one ohm if there is one ampere of current in a circuit when one volt is applied. By applying a known voltage, V, to a circuit and measuring the current, I, the meter scale can be calibrated to read in ohms of resistance. This is the basic principle of an ohmmeter.

Basic Ohmmeter Circuit

The basic ohmmeter circuit is shown in *Figure 1-17*. The ohmmeter circuit applies voltage from a self-contained battery to a series connection consisting of a known resistance (R_K) to the unknown resistance (R_U). The meter movement determines the value of the unknown resistance by measuring the current in the circuit.

Ohmmeters are very useful in servicing electronic equipment by making quick measurements of resistance values. The resistance values that can be measured with the ohmmeter vary from a fraction of an ohm to 100 megohms or more. The accuracy is seldom better than 3%; therefore, they generally are not suitable for measurements that require high accuracy.

Since ohmmeters contain their own power source, and depend on their internal calibrated circuits for accuracy, they should be used only on passive circuits; that is, circuits that are not connected to power sources. *Connecting them into circuits with other power sources destroys the calibration and can very easily destroy the ohmmeter.*

Series Ohmmeter

Let's look again at the basic series-type ohmmeter circuit shown in *Figure 1-17*. Notice that when the test leads are open (R_U equals infinity), there is no current through the meter. The meter needle at rest indicates an infinite resistance.

When the test leads are shorted ($R_U = 0$), there is a full-scale deflection of the needle indicating a zero resistance measurement. The typical meter scale is shown in *Figure 1-17*. The purpose of R_C is to allow adjustment to zero on the scale to compensate for a changing battery potential due to aging, and for lead and fuse resistance. The purpose of R_K is to limit the current through the meter circuit to full scale when the test leads are shorted.

Figure 1-17. A Simple Series Ohmmeter

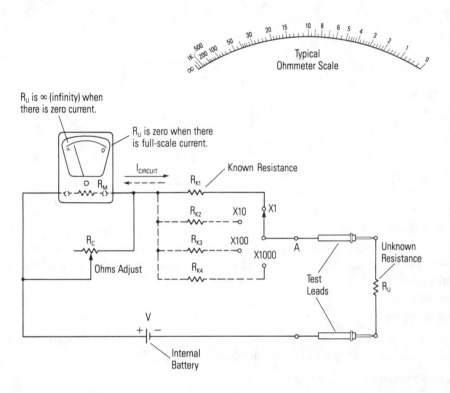

It is convenient to use a value for R_K in the design of the series ohmmeter such that when an unknown resistance equal to R_K is measured, the meter will deflect to half scale. Therefore, when the leads are shorted together, the meter deflection will be full scale. Using this criteria, multiple ranges for the ohmmeter can be provided by switching to different values of R_K as shown in *Figure 1-17*. Each R_K would set the half-scale value for the respective resistance range, and provides the scale multiplier.

Shunt Ohmmeter

The shunt-type ohmmeter is often found in laboratories because it is particularly suited to the measurement of very low value resistors. The circuit for a shunt-type ohmmeter is shown in *Figure 1-18*. In this circuit, current has two paths, one through the meter and one through R_X, if there is one. If the leads are open from A to B ($R_X = \infty$), then the meter movement reads full scale (adjusted by R_1). This is marked as infinity. If the leads are shorted, the meter current drops to zero and the resistance is marked as 0 ohms. When a value of unknown resistance R_X is placed across the terminals A and B, it causes the meter to deflect to some point below full scale. For example, if R_X equals R_M, then the meter movement would read half scale.

Figure 1-18. A Simple Shunt Ohmmeter

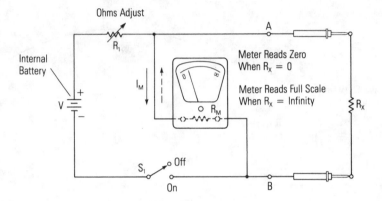

The scales for the two types of ohmmeters are exactly opposite. The series ohmmeter scale has 0 ohms on the right while the shunt-type has the 0 ohms position on its left. This becomes a good way to identify the type of ohmmeter you might be using.

AC METERS

The most practical means for measuring commonly used ac voltages is by combining a highly sensitive D'Arsonval meter movement and a rectifier.

The Purpose of the Rectifier

The purpose of the rectifier is to change the alternating current to direct current. The D'Arsonval meter movement is a dc movement because of the permanent magnet which sets up the field for the moving coil. The method of using a rectifier to convert the dc movement to measuring ac is very attractive because the D'Arsonval meter movement has a much higher sensitivity than other types of meters that may be used to measure ac, such as an electrodynamometer or the moving iron-vane type meters.

● Bridge-Type Rectifier

The circuit of *Figure 1-19* makes use of a bridge-type rectifier which provides full-wave rectification. The bridge is generally made of germanium or silicon diodes. Since a D'Arsonval meter movement provides a deflection that is proportional to the "average" value of the dc current. In practice, most alternating currents and voltages are expressed in effective values. As a result, the meter scale is calibrated in terms of the effective value of a sine wave even though the meter is responding to the average value. Effective value is also referred to as RMS (Root-Mean-Squares) value.

Figure 1-19. AC Voltmeter Using a Bridge Rectifier

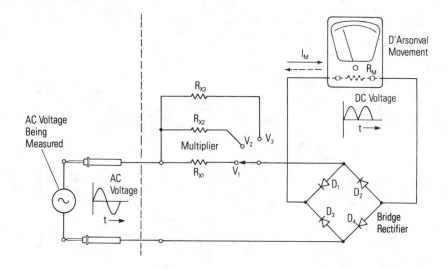

A conversion factor which will relate the average and the RMS values of a sine wave may be found by dividing the RMS value by the average value:

$$\frac{E_{rms}}{E_{avg}} = 1.11$$

This conversion factor is valid only for sinusoidal ac measurements.

Multirange AC Voltmeters

As shown in *Figure 1-19*, just as for dc voltmeters, multiplier resistors can be added to provide multirange ac voltmeters. A more common circuit used for commercial ac voltmeters is shown in *Figure 1-20*. This circuit uses rectifiers to convert the ac voltages to dc in just a little different way. There is current through the meter movement as D_1 conducts on the positive half-cycle, while D_2 conducts on the negative cycle to bypass the meter. R_s is connected across the meter movement in order to desensitize the meter causing it to draw more current through the diode D_1. This moves the operating point on the diode curve up into a more linear portion of the characteristic curve. Multiple ranges can be provided by having various multiplier resistors for the required ranges. AC meters normally have lower internal resistance than dc meters with the same meter movement.

CALIBRATION, PARALLAX, ETC.

Having covered some of the types of analog meters, let's discuss several items that apply generally. Calibration is one of these.

Figure 1-20. A Practical AC Voltmeter Circuit

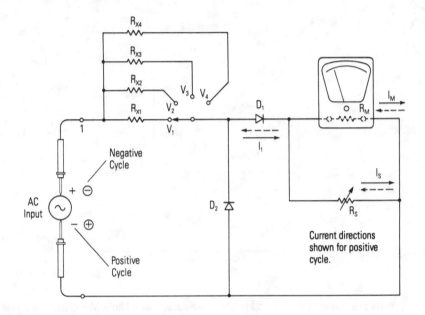

The sensitivity of the meter movement may be determined and the meter calibrated as shown in *Figure 1-8*. Calibration requires a standard. In this case, it is the current meter used to indicate the current. It is advisable to calibrate the lowest dc current range first since all ranges of the instrument will be seriously in error if the basic current range is not accurate. Errors on the various scale may be noted so that readings may be adjusted accordingly. If errors are great, shunts and multipliers would have to be modified inside the meter.

Parallax Error

Parallax error in reading the position of a meter's needle on the scale is due to the position of the head and eyes over the needle. The most accurate reading is obtained when the head is positioned perpendicular to the scales and directly over the needle. To assure this, many meters have mirrors imbedded in the scales so the needle can be aligned with its image in the mirror. The head is positioned correctly when this alignment is accomplished.

Weak Batteries

Internal batteries will need to be replaced if the "Ohms Adjust" no longer adjusts the needle to R = 0 or R = ∞. This becomes a good indicator of battery condition.

SUMMARY

Now that we know the characteristics of analog meters that measure current, voltage and resistance, let's look at digital meters.

DVM - THE BASIC CONCEPTS

BASIC DVM

A typical digital multimeter was shown in *Figure 1-2*. It had a single rotary selector switch that selected whether the meter was to be used as a dc voltmeter, dc ammeter, ac voltmeter, or ohmmeter. It selected the full-scale range of the measurement automatically. Another digital multimeter is shown in *Figure 2-1*. It has a digital display, an ON-OFF switch, test jacks to accept test leads, a measurement function selection, and a full-scale range selection. It differs from the meter in *Figure 1-2* in that it has two selector switches. One is for the measurement function, and the other for the full-scale range. It also measures ac current as well as voltage, while the meter in *Figure 1-2* only measured ac voltage.

Comparison to Analog Meters

Unlike the analog meter that has a needle deflecting along a scale, each of these digital multimeters, as is the case for all digital multimeters, has a digital display. The measurement value is shown in both cases displayed as a number with four digits. On the lowest full-scale range, the measurement is read on the display to an accuracy of three decimal places.

Unlike the analog meter, digital multitesters have an ON-OFF power switch. They contain electronic circuits to produce their measurement value rather than an electromechanical meter movement. As a result, they need internal batteries to supply power for the electronics as well as an energy source to supply current for resistance measurements when the meter is used as an ohmmeter. The ON-OFF switch connects the power source to the circuits. Like the analog meter, the digital multitesters have range and function selector switches and jacks to accept test leads.

Figure 2-1. Digital Multimeter

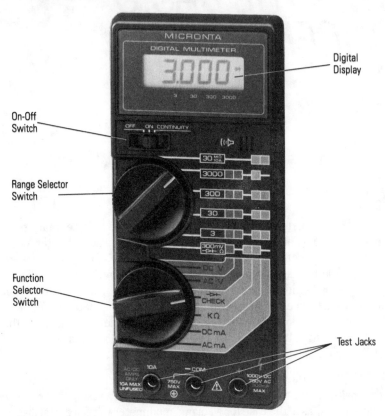

DVM Characteristics

Several important characteristics result from the fact that digital multitesters are electronic. One characteristic is that they are basically voltmeters, and when used as ammeters or ohmmeters, the circuit arrangement is such that the DVM is used as a voltmeter. A second characteristic is that the DVM has a high internal resistance on all functional ranges. As will be shown in Chapter 3, having a high internal resistance is a very desirable characteristic because circuit loading is usually negligible when using a DVM.

The third and fourth characteristics are due to the digital display. Because the display is digital there is no parallax reading error, or error due to interprolation between scale marks as on an analog meter. Because the display is digital, the conversion accuracy is within ± one digit on any of the scales used. The accuracy due to the display remains constant over all ranges and doesn't vary. As a result, overall accuracies of DVMs are typically 0.05% to 1.5% as compared to 3-4% for analog meters.

A fifth characteristic relates to the special functions that are available. An audio tone that sounds when measuring circuit continuity is a common example. A special check for semiconductor junctions is another. The meter in *Figure 1-2* has the semiconductor junction test, while the meter in *Figure 2-1* has both special functions.

HOW A DVM WORKS

A block diagram of a typical digital voltmeter is shown in *Figure 2-2*. Either dc or ac voltages can be measured. Let's look at measuring a dc voltage first.

The test probes measure the dc voltage, bring it into the DVM through a signal conditioner, and couple it to a circuit called an analog to digital or A to D (A/D) converter. The A/D converter accepts a voltage and changes it to a digital code that represents the magnitude of the voltage. The digital code is used to generate the numerical digits that show the measured value in the digital display.

Figure 2-2. Block Diagram of a Basic Digital Voltmeter

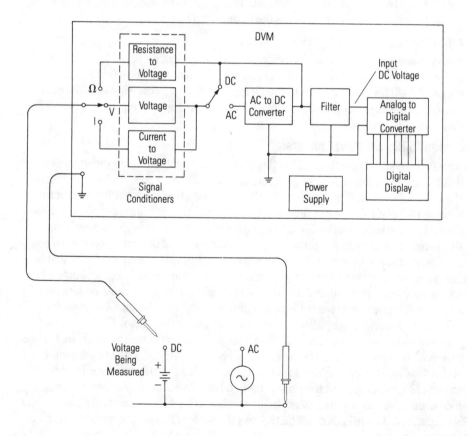

Digital Display

An easy way to understand how a DVM works is to begin at the display. *Figure 2-3a* shows a common way to display a numerical digit. A 7-segment array of elements is used to form the digits. The array elements may be vacuum fluorescent, electroluminescent, or plasma display elements. But very common displays for portable DVMs used in the laboratory or service shop are light emitting diodes (LEDs) or liquid crystal displays (LCDs). Liquid crystal displays use very little power, but must have ambient light or back illumination to operate the display. LED displays use much more power, but are much brighter and not easily washed out in bright sunlight.

As shown in *Figure 2-3a* (which is a typical LED display schematic), a power source is connected to each LED segment, and each LED segment is excited by passing current through it. In the example shown, the segments necessary to display a numeral 2 are grounded and current through them causes the segments to emit light. The table shown in *Figure 2-3b* lists the segments that must be excited to display any of the numerals from 0 to 9. As shown in the example of *Figure 2-3a*, a decoder establishes the proper segments that must be grounded. The decoder has an input digital code that represents the numeral required.

● BCD Codes

A very common code used in digital systems to represent numerals is a 4-bit binary coded decimal (BCD) code. The BCD code for the numerals from 0 to 9 is shown in *Figure 2-3b*. This code, if fed into the decoder of *Figure 2-3a*, will cause the decoder to ground the proper segments of the digit display to display the proper numeral for the table of *Figure 2-3b*.

Analog to Digital (A/D) Conversion

Now that we know how the BCD codes provide the input to display the numerals, let's find out how the codes are generated in the A/D converter. A block diagram is shown in *Figure 2-4*. The table shows the BCD code that is output for each of the four digits when a dc voltage between 0 and 2 volts (1.999 volts) is applied at the input. The resolution of the DVM is one millivolt, which means that a new 4-digit BCD code is generated for each change in one millivolt of the input voltage. *Figure 2-4* does not show each one millivolt 4-digit code, but lists the codes that would be generated for the four digits for each one tenth of a volt. In addition, it shows some special example values (0.001, 0.578, 1.234, 1.667 and 1.999) to help understand what the A/D converter output is like. There is a separate 4-digit BCD code for each one millivolt, but, for simplicity, they are not all included in *Figure 2-4*.

If the input voltage to the A/D converter is 1.234 volts, the four-digit BCD code that would be generated at the output would be 0001 0010 0011 0100 as shown. Each of the 4-bit BCD codes representing a digit is coupled to a decoder, like the one shown in *Figure 2-3a*, and the proper numeral displayed for the respective digit. Individual logic gates in the A/D converter control the decimal point. If a logic 1 level is output, the decimal point will be ON. As the scales change, the decimal point energized changes.

Figure 2-3. 7-Segment Digit Display

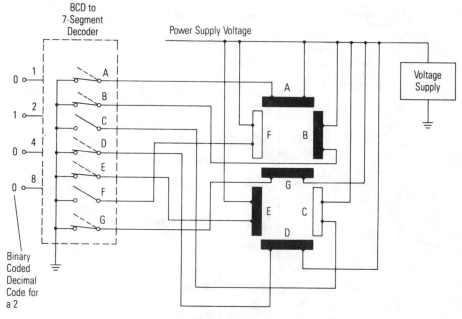

a. Segment Schematic
(The digit 2 being displayed)

Digit	Segment							BCD Code
	A	B	C	D	E	F	G	
0	●	●	●	●	●	●		0000
1		●	●					0001
2	●	●		●	●		●	0010
3	●	●	●	●			●	0011
4		●	●			●	●	0100
5	●		●	●		●	●	0101
6			●	●	●	●	●	0110
7	●	●	●					0111
8	●	●	●	●	●	●	●	1000
9	●	●	●			●	●	1001

● Means segment is grounded

b. Excitation Table for Digits

The display techniques and the outputs of the A/D converter shown in *Figure 2-3* and *Figure 2-4* are not the only way a DVM can produce the conversion and display. There are scanning techniques and multiplexing techniques so that the digit codes are transferred in sequence along fewer bus lines, but the more direct way was chosen to make it easier to illustrate and explain the basic concepts.

Figure 2-4. A/D Converter with 0-2 Volts Input and 4 Digit Output Codes

A/D Converter

Voltage (in volts)	Digit Code 1		Digit Code 2		Digit Code 3		Digit Code 4
1.999	0001	1	1001	0	1001	0	1001
1.900	0001	1	1001	0	0000	0	0000
1.800	0001	1	1000	0	0000	0	0000
1.700	0001	1	0111	0	0000	0	0000
1.667	0001	1	0110	0	0110	0	0111
1.600	0001	1	0110	0	0000	0	0000
1.500	0001	1	0101	0	0000	0	0000
1.400	0001	1	0100	0	0000	0	0000
1.300	0001	1	0011	0	0000	0	0000
1.234	0001	1	0010	0	0011	0	0100
1.200	0001	1	0010	0	0000	0	0000
1.100	0001	1	0001	0	0000	0	0000
1.000	0001	1	0000	0	0000	0	0000
0.900	0000	1	1001	0	0000	0	0000
0.800	0000	1	1000	0	0000	0	0000
0.700	0000	1	0111	0	0000	0	0000
0.600	0000	1	0110	0	0000	0	0000
0.578	0000	1	0101	0	0111	0	1000
0.500	0000	1	0101	0	0000	0	0000
0.400	0000	1	0100	0	0000	0	0000
0.300	0000	1	0011	0	0000	0	0000
0.200	0000	1	0010	0	0000	0	0000
0.100	0000	1	0001	0	0000	0	0000
0.001	0000	1	0000	0	0000	0	0001
0.000	0000	1	0000	0	0000	0	0000
Decimal Point Active for Scale Shown		DP_1 2V		DP_2 20V		DP_3 200V	

0-2 Volts

Digit 1: 1, 2, 4, 8
DP_1 Decimal Pt. 1
Digit 2: 1, 2, 4, 8
DP_2 Decimal Pt. 2
Digit 3: 1, 2, 4, 8
DP_3 Decimal Pt. 3
Digit 4: 1, 2, 4, 8

THE A/D CONVERSION PROCESS

There are a number of techniques used to perform the actual conversion process. Staircase integrating, continuous balance, successive approximations, dual-slope, voltage-to-frequency converters are the names of some of them. We do not have space to cover all of these, so we will pick the staircase and the dual-slope converter because these demonstrate the basic concepts the best.

Staircase Converter

Figure 2-5 shows the block diagram of a staircase converter. It consists of a comparator, a clock gate G, a clock generator, a binary counter, and a digital to analog converter. The output is coupled to a digital display. The digital to analog converter does the opposite of the analog to digital converter. It takes the digital code output

Figure 2-5. Staircase A/D Converter

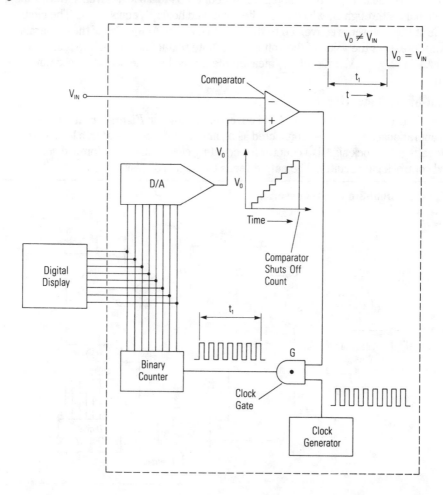

from the stages of the binary counter and converts it to an analog voltage. Each time the binary counter increases its count by one, the output voltage V_O increases by a millivolt. V_O is one input to the comparator; the input voltage V_{IN} is the other input to the comparator.

● V_O Not Equal to V_{IN}

When the input voltage V_{IN} is first applied to be measured, V_O is zero, and the output of the comparator is at a 1 logic level because V_O if not equal to V_{IN}. Since the comparator 1 output is an input to the AND clock gate G, the clock signal appearing on the other G input will appear on the gate output and feed into the binary counter. The binary counter counts the clock pulses, and through the D/A converter begins to increase V_O by 1 millivolt per count. Thus, the name staircase converter.

● V_O Equal to V_{IN}

When V_O is equal to V_{IN}, the comparator output drops to a 0 logic level, turns off the clock pulses through G, which stops the count and holds V_O equal to V_{IN}. The digital code at the counter is converted to the necessary code for display of the numerals that represents the value of the voltage V_{IN}. Note that it takes time t_1 to reach the point where $V_O = V_{IN}$; therefore, measurements can be done only at a maximum rate.

Dual-Slope Converter

A block diagram of a dual-slope A/D converter is shown in *Figure 2-6*. It consists of an operational amplifier, A, connected as an integrator, a comparator, a logic gate (G) for gating the clock signal, a counter for counting clock pulses, a reference voltage, and control logic circuitry. The output feeds to a digital display.

Figure 2-6. Dual-Slope A/D Converter

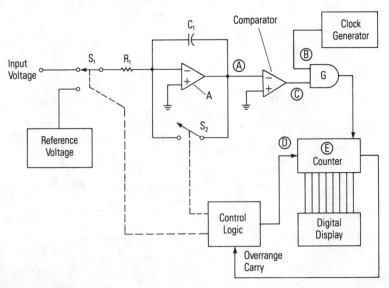

As with the staircase converter, the magnitude of the input voltage measured is determined by the number of clock pulses counted. The resultant counter code is then converted to the appropriate code to display the proper digits on the digital display.

The number of pulses counted is determined by a start count control signal (D) in *Figure 2-6* which allows the counter to start counting, and a comparator output signal (C) which stops counting by gating off the clock pulses. The timing is shown in *Figure 2-7*.

Figure 2-7. Dual-Slope Converter Operation

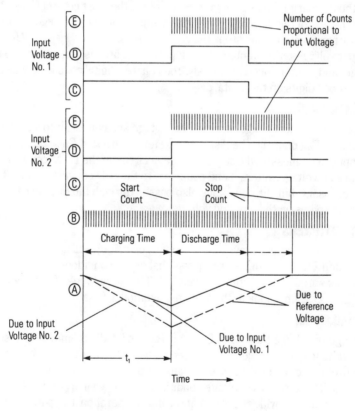

Legend:
- Ⓐ Integrator Output
- Ⓑ Clock Signal
- Ⓒ Comparator Output
- Ⓓ Counter Start Control
- Ⓔ Number of Counts

● Basic Operation

The basic concept of the operation is as follows: S_2 is a switch that shorts out C_1 so that there initially is no charge on C_1. When a measurement is made, S_2 is open, and S_1 is connected to the input voltage for a period of time t_1 shown in *Figure 2-7*. In time t_1, capacitor C_1 charges at a constant rate and to a magnitude of voltage determined by the input voltage. At the end of t_1, S_1 is switched to a reference voltage that is opposite in polarity to the input voltage. This reference voltage discharges capacitor C_1 at a constant rate. The time that it takes to discharge C back to the initial zero level (and just a few millivolts more because the comparator output must switch states) is proportional to the input voltage magnitude. The charging and discharging curves for two different input voltages are shown in *Figure 2-7*.

When the discharge time starts (at the end of t_1), the start control (D) starts the counter. At the end of the discharge time, the comparator output (C) goes to a low logic level, turns off gate G, and stops the counter. As shown in *Figure 2-7* for two different input voltages, the number of clock pulses counted is proportional to the input voltage, and as mentioned previously, the counter digital code is decoded to display the proper digits on the digital display.

AC MEASUREMENTS

The A/D converter is designed to accept a dc voltage and convert it to a digital code so the corresponding digits can be displayed. Referring back to *Figure 2-2*, we see that if the input to be measured is an ac voltage, a circuit in the DVM converts the ac voltage to a dc voltage, filters it and couples it to the A/D converter. It isn't absolutely necessary, but the dc voltage also passes through the filter in case there are some noise spikes on the input dc voltage.

SIGNAL CONDITIONERS

Because the A/D converter always needs an input dc voltage, all uses of the DVM as a voltmeter, ammeter, or ohmmeter requires that signal conditioners be used to convert the measured quantity into a dc voltage. The three types of conditioners are shown in *Figure 2-2*. Let's look at the voltage conditioner first.

Voltage Conditioner

Since the range of voltage that the A/D converter can handle is limited by design — zero to two volts in our example — measured voltages greater than two volts will need to be attenuated, and voltages less than one-third to one-fifth of a volt will need to be amplified. Therefore, the voltage conditioner, a shown in *Figure 2-8*, is made up of a voltage divider to provide the attenuation and an operational amplifier to provide the amplification. There are five voltage ranges — 0.2V, 2V, 20V, 200V and 2000V.

The gain of the operational amplifier is set by the equation

$$A = -\frac{R_F}{R_i}$$

where R_i is the input resistance. The minus sign means that the output signal is 180° out of phase from the input signal. R_F and R_i (made up due to R_2, R_3 and R_7) are chosen so that A equals one on the 2V range. With unity gain for the amplifier (A = 1), the input voltage is reproduced directly at the amplifier output and coupled to the A/D converter. On the 20V, 200V, and 2000V range, R_3 and R_7 are chosen such that the gain of the amplifier is unity again, just as for the 2V range (R_F does not change). The ratio of R_4, R_5 and R_6 to R_7 is set so that with 20 volts, 200 volts, and 2000 volts, respectively on the input, the input voltage to the amplifier will be 2 volts. For the 0.2V range, R_1 is chosen so the gain of the amplifier is ten.

The voltage conditioner will work equally well for dc and ac voltage measurements over the frequency range specified for the DVM as long as the stray capacitance in the circuitry is kept to a minimum. Of course, the ac voltage at the output of the signal conditioner must be converted back to dc before it is coupled to the A/D converter.

AC to DC Conversion

Many VOMs, multitesters and DVMs that have rectifier type circuits have scales that are calibrated in RMS values for ac measurements, but actually are measuring the average value of the input voltage and are depending on the voltage to be a sine wave. These instruments are in error if the input voltage has some other shape than a sine wave.

There are DVMs that are manufactured that measure the true RMS value of input voltages regardless of the shape of the waveform. They measure the dc and ac component of the input waveforms; therefore, the measured value is the heating power of an ac voltage that is equivalent to the heating power of a dc voltage equal to the RMS value--the definition of an RMS voltage. Check the specifications of a DVM that you are using to determine if it measures true RMS voltages. If it does not, be wary of the measurement if the input voltage is not a sine wave or if it has a dc component.

Figure 2-8. Voltage Conditioner

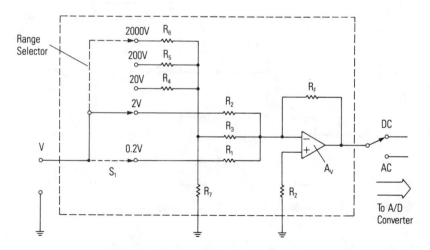

Current Conditioners

The signal conditioning circuit for measuring current is shown in *Figure 2-9*. The current conditioner changes the current to be measured into a voltage by passing the unknown current through a precision resistance (R_1, R_2, R_3 or R_4) and measuring the voltage developed across the resistor. The range switch determines the resistor used for each range. When the proper current range is selected, the proper resistance is selected so that the voltage out of the current conditioner will be within the range required by the A/D converter. The resistors used are a special type of high power precision resistor used as current shunts.

The position of the AC/DC switch determines the route the voltage output from the current conditioner takes to reach the input of the A/D converter. A high current range, such as 10 amps, usually is measured using a special input jack to which a special resistor is connected. An operational amplifier with a fixed gain prevents loading of the current sensing resistors by the A/D converter.

Resistance Conditioners

The basic circuit for the signal conditioner that the DVM uses for resistance measurements is shown in *Figure 2-10a*. The voltage V and the resistance R_s form a constant current source for the unknown resistor. A constant current through a given resistor will produce a set voltage drop. For example, if the constant current is 1 milliampere (0.001A) through a 1000 ohm resistor, the voltage drop across the 1000 ohm resistor is 1 volt. That's exactly what the DVM does to measure resistance, it measures the voltage across an unknown resistance when there is a known constant current through it. The voltage source, the series resistance, and the voltage range are changed as the full-scale range of resistance to be measured by the DVM is changed.

Figure 2-9. Current Conditioner

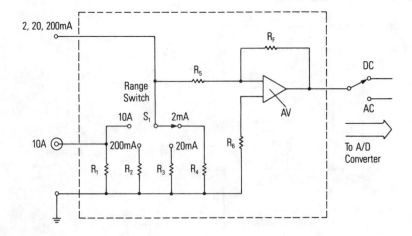

An alternate circuit found in some popular DVMs is shown in *Figure 2-10b*. It uses a ratio method to measure the value of the unknown resistor. If an unknown resistor R_X is placed in series with a known reference resistor R_R across a known voltage source V_S, the ratio of the voltage drop across the unknown resistor, V_X, to the voltage across the reference resistor, V_R, is equal to the ratio of R_X to R_R. This is expressed by the equation

$$\frac{R_X}{R_R} = \frac{V_X}{V_R}$$

Figure 2-10. Resistance Conditioner

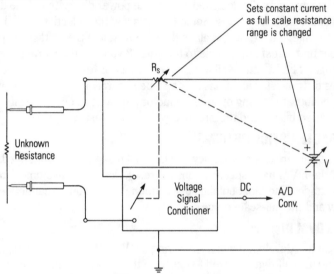

a. Basic Ohmmeter Circuit

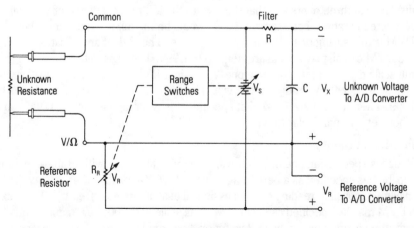

b. Ratio Measurement Circuit

Rearranging gives the value of R_X in terms of the known reference resistor and the voltage ratio.

$$R_X = R_R \frac{V_X}{V_R}$$

Extra circuits are designed into the A/D converter so it can be used to measure the voltage ratio V_X/V_R and calculate the unknown resistance, R_X. R_R and V_S are changed for different resistance ranges, but are known values for each measurement calculation.

● Hi-Lo Ranges

The test circuits are carefully designed so that the power dissipated in the device under test is limited to safe values. Some DVMs allow the selection of a HI/LO measurement range. These ranges allow the user to select the voltage drop across the component under test at full scale to be either 2 volts on the HI range or 0.1 volts on the LO range. The LO range allows in-circuit resistor testing without forward biasing diodes or transistor junctions that may be in parallel with the resistor. The HI ranges allow deliberate testing of semiconductor junctions to determine if they are forward or reverse biased and their respective junction resistances.

BASIC CHARACTERISTICS OF DVMS

Besides the characteristics of accuracy and internal resistance (input impedance) that VOMs have, the DVM have specifications for resolution, response time, protection, and burden voltage. The most unique specifications are the ones that define the digital display and the full-scale range.

Digits of the DVM Display

A strange term has developed when specifying a DVM. It concerns the digital display. The term "half-digit" is used to describe the display capability of the DVM and the reading beyond full-scale that it can display. This is called overranging.

If a DVM is classified as a 3½ digit DVM, it means that the full-scale reading is displayed in three digits and that the digit to the left of the 3 digits for full-scale is restricted in range. For example, 0.999 would be the full-scale reading when the DVM is measuring one volt on the 1 volt range. The ½ digit specification means that the DVM can display a measurement up to 1.999. The digit to the left of the three full-scale digits is restricted to a one. A 4½ digit DVM would have a capability to read a value to 19999. A 3¾ digit DVM would have the capability to read a value as high as 3999. Therefore, the ½ or ¾ digit specifies the overranging that the DVM can read when set on a particular range.

Full-Scale Range

Range is specified in one of two ways: (1) a full-scale range with usable overrange capabilities specified as a percentage, typically 100%; or (2) full scale specified as the maximum possible reading encompassing all usable ranges, often 1.999. For example, a DVM may be specified as having 1 volt full scale with 100% overrange, thus indicating useful operations to 2 volts; or the same DVM may be simply specified as having a 2 volt full scale.

Some ranges may not be used to full scale. For example, the higher voltage ranges may be limited because of the voltage breakdown of internal components. A DVM with a 1999 volt full scale range may not be used to read over 1000 volts because divider resistors cannot withstand over 1000 volts breakdown. The capability may be even lower on AC because of peak voltages.

● *Overranging*

Overranging was instituted to take full advantage of the upper limits of a range. It also provides better accuracy at the top of a range. In other words, overranging allows a DVM to measure voltage values above the normal range switch transfer points without the necessity of having to change ranges. It allows the meter to keep the same resolution for values near the transfer points.

The extent to which the overrange is possible is expressed in terms of the percentage of the full-scale range. Overranging from 5-300% is available depending upon the make and model of the DVM.

Accuracy and Resolution

Simple accuracy specifications are given as "plus/minus percentage of full scale, plus/minus one digit." The "plus/minus one digit" portion of the specification is caused by an error in the digital counting circuit. The "plus/minus percentage of full scale" includes ranging and A/D conversion errors.

The "plus/minus one digit" also relates to the resolution of the DVM. The resolution of an instrument is directly limited by the number of digits in the display. A 3½ digit DVM has a resolution of one part in 2,000 or 0.05% which means that it can resolve a measurement of 1999 millivolts down to 1 millivolt. A 4 ½ digit instrument has a resolution of one part in 20,000, or 0.005%.

A 2½ or a 3 digit DVM is considered approximately equivalent to a good VOM multitester as far as accuracy and resolution are concerned. Accuracy generally lies between 0.5% and 1.5% and resolution to 0.5%. The 3½ and 4½ meters generally have accuracy one order of magnitude higher; that is, between 0.5% and 0.05% with 0.05% resolution. A resolution and accuracy of this amount will generally suffice for most service work today. A 4½ digit, 5½ digit DVM generally indicate an accuracy of 0.05% and better with resolution of 0.005%. These are indeed considered laboratory instruments. They usually are specified with a "plus/minus percent of reading, plus/minus percent of full scale, plus/minus one digit" specification. They also may have specifications that qualify the accuracy at temperatures other that 25°C.

A DVM has essentially the same accuracy on ac that it does on dc voltage measurements while the accuracy of an analog meter is most assuredly less accurate on the ac voltage measurements. Accuracy will also depend upon the frequency response or bandwidth of the DVM, and on the ac waveshape when the meter does not measure true RMS voltages.

Input Impedance

DVMs have an input impedance of at least one megohm and more commonly 10 megohms. This holds true on dc measurements and on ac measurements over the frequency range specified for the DVM.

Response Time

Response time is the number of seconds required for the instrument to settle to its rated accuracy. The response time consists of two factors: (1) the basic cycle rate of the A/D converter; and (2) the time required to charge capacitances in the input circuit. Instead of response time, some manufacturers simply give a number of conversions per second.

Protection

Meter protection circuits prevent accidental damage to the DVM. The protection circuit allows the instrument to absorb a reasonable amount of abuse without affecting its performance. The specification of input protection indicates the amount of voltage overload which may be applied to any function or range without damage. A separate dc limit may be indicated to cover input coupling capacitor breakdown. Overloads from sources outside the specified frequency range of the instrument may not have as great a protection range. The current measuring circuitry is usually protected by a fast-blowing fuse in series with the input lead.

Ammeter Errors Due to Burden Voltage

When a meter is placed in series with a circuit to measure current, an error caused by the voltage drop across the meter is due to the meter and its current shunts and any protective fuses that are connected in series. This voltage drop is called a burden voltage. The full scale burden voltages for the instrument are usually very low — 0.3 volts for low ranges and from 0.5 to 0.9 volts for the high current ranges. These voltage drops, of course, can affect the accuracy of a current measurement if the current source is unregulated and the resistance of the current meter represents a significant part ($\frac{1}{1000}$) of the source resistance. This burden voltage error can be minimized by selecting the highest current range that provides the required resolution. Some manufacturers specify "voltage burden," which is the maximum voltage drop across the meter input terminals caused by full-scale current. Other manufacturers specify series resistance. Either is adequate as long as the value is specified for each current range.

Displays

We have already mentioned LED and LCD displays. The light-emitting diode (LED) has been one of the most popular displays in use with DVMs because of its brightness, excellent contrast and low cost. Other displays have historically been 10-character neon displays (NIXIE) and the 7-segment neon display. The disadvantages of these displays are higher cost combined with the need for a high-voltage power supply. Neon, as well as fluorescent displays, tend to generate slight RF interference noise. The liquid crystal display (LCD) is becoming very popular because of its very low power drain and decreasing cost. The newer types do not wash out in bright sunlight. However, a disadvantage is that many of them will freeze at fairly moderate temperatures and become completely useless.

SPECIAL FEATURES

Auto Ranging

Auto ranging automatically adjusts the meter's measuring circuits to the correct voltage, current or resistance ranges. One technique is for the DVM to start on the lowest range and automatically move to the next higher range when auto range takes place. A special feature of some auto range DVMs (Radio Shack No. 22-195 shown in *Figure 2-11*) is a RANGE CONTROL function which overides the auto range. This is useful when a series of measurements are made within a specific range.

If the upper limit of the range being held is exceeded, the meter produces a series of beeps if the buzzer switch is ON. A portion of the display will flash indicating an overflow error. Pushing the control button switch to the AUTO position releases the RANGE CONTROL.

Figure 2-11. Auto-Range DVM

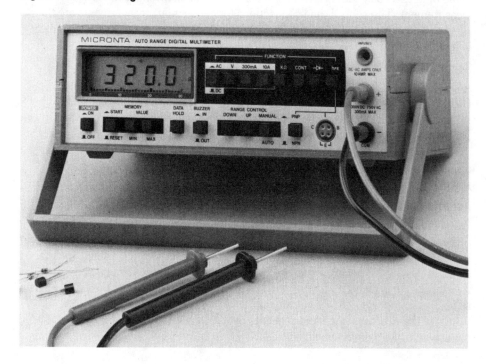

Auto Polarity

The automatic polarity feature further reduces measurement error and possible instrument damage because of overload due to a voltage of reverse polarity. A + or – activated on the digital display indicates the polarity and eliminates the need for a POLARITY switch setting, or reversing leads.

Hold That Reading!

Many digital multitesters have a HOLD feature that is operated remotely by means of a special HOLD button included on one of the test leads. It is particularly useful when making measurements in a difficult area because readings can be captured and held and read when convenient.

In some DVMs, the hold signal sets an internal latch that captures the data. When the A/D gets to the point in its cycle where data is to be displayed, the state of the internal latch is sampled. New data is not transferred while the latch is in the hold state. In other DVMs, the hold feature stops the instrument clock. The last value displayed on the LCD remains displayed until the ground is removed from the input terminal.

Conductance Measurements

Some meters display the reciprocal of resistance; that is, a conductance measurement. The controls and connections for conduction measurements are the same as for resistance. The output, however, is displayed in siemens, the reciprocal of resistance (previously called mhos).

Semiconductor Testing

A DIODE CHECK or SEMICONDUCTOR CHECK function appears on some DVMs. Most DVMs have an ohmmeter voltage of greater than 1.5 volts. Thus, continuity for most diodes and transistors in the forward bias direction may be checked.

Some DVMs have a special feature when in the DIODE CHECK position that displays a voltage value which is essentially the forward bias voltage of the PN junction.

Audible Continuity Test

Often DVMs have an audible continuity function. With the DVM set to measure resistance and the CONTINUITY switch activated, when the probes are touched together the DVM emits an audible sound. This electronic sound is used to look for short circuits or for tracing for an open circuit. Any time the continuity circuit resistance is less than a minimum amount, usually 200 or 300 ohms, the DVM emits an audible sound when the circuit is complete.

Now that we know the basic concepts of VOMs and DVMs let's move on to find out how to make measurements.

ABOUT MULTITESTER MEASUREMENTS

This chapter deals with how to make measurements with a multitester, whether it is with an analog meter as described in Chapter 1 or with a digital meter described in Chapter 2. However, before discussing the actual measurements, it might be beneficial to review three basic fundamentals of dc circuits. They are: Ohm's law, series and parallel circuits, and polarity.

OHM'S LAW

In the early eighteen hundreds, a German physicist by the name of Georg Simon Ohm discovered the basic relationship of voltage, current and resistance in a dc circuit which he expressed as

$$I = \frac{V}{R}$$

Stated in words, it said that the current I in a dc circuit varied directly with the voltage V applied to the circuit and inversely with the resistance R in the circuit. With a given resistance, if voltage is increased, current will increase; with a given voltage, if resistance is increased, current will decrease.

SERIES CIRCUITS

In a series circuit like the one shown in *Figure 3-1*, there is only one current path. As shown, the conventional current direction through the circuit is from the positive terminal of the battery to the negative terminal. Electron current is opposite, the negatively charged electrons are attracted to the positive terminal of the battery and released from the negative terminal.

The amount of current in the series current can be found by dividing the voltage (10 volts) by the total resistance in the circuit (100 ohms) just like Ohm's law says:

$$I = \frac{10V}{100\Omega}$$

$$I = 0.1A$$

Figure 3-1. Simple DC Series Circuit

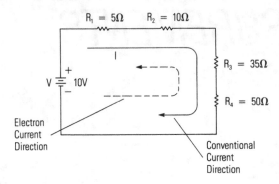

The current is 0.1 amperes. There is the same current throughout the series circuit and through each series circuit component. The current has one path through all the circuit components in series.

PARALLEL CIRCUITS

Parallel circuits are different. Current in a parallel circuit has more than one path. The different paths are called branches. *Figure 3-2* is a simple parallel circuit. As with the series circuit, it has a 10 volt battery to supply the current, but the current is through two branches — one through R_1 and the other through R_2. The total current I_T from the battery divides into the two branch currents, I_1 and I_2. The total current I_T is the sum of the two branch currents. Therefore,

$$I_T = I_1 + I_2$$

Each branch current can be calculated by using Ohm's law. For example,

$$I_1 = \frac{10V}{100\Omega} = 0.1A$$

and

$$I_2 = \frac{10V}{400\Omega} = 0.025A$$

Figure 3-2. Simple Parallel Circuit

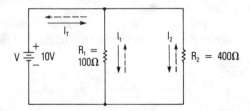

The total current is

$$I_T = 0.1A + 0.025A$$
$$I_T = 0.125A$$

One tenth ampere is in the R_1 branch through R_1; 25 thousandths of an ampere is in the R_2 branch through R_2. The total current of 0.125A can also be expressed as 125 $\times 10^{-3}$ amperes. The common abbreviation of "milli" is substituted for 10^{-3}; therefore, the current is 125 milliamperes. 100 milliamperes is in the R_1 branch and 25 milliamperes is in the R_2 branch.

Note that the voltage across each branch is the same. That is a common characteristic of parallel circuits, *the voltage is the same across parallel branches*.

POLARITY

When making dc measurements with your multimeter or multitester, you will be concerned about observing polarity so that your meter will read correctly. Current must be in the proper direction through a dc meter to cause it to read up scale. If polarity is observed properly, then the meter will read up scale. Otherwise, the meter will peg against the stop that restricts it from deflecting down scale. Digital voltmeters do not have this restriction; they display the polarity of the voltage, but the reference point for the measurement is still very important.

Reference Point

A reference point is a point in a circuit to which the voltage at other points in the circuit is compared. This is demonstrated best by an example. *Figure 3-3* combines a pictorial and schematic of the common electrical system for starting your car. The negative terminal of the battery is connected to the automobile chassis which becomes a connecting link of the circuit. It is like a common wire connecting all points marked "chassis ground." This becomes an excellent reference point for all measurements in this automotive circuit. As shown in *Figure 3-3*, the common or negative terminal of a VOM is connected to the negative terminal (A) of the battery through chassis ground (A¹). A voltage measurement is made at point B to measure the battery voltage by placing the positive probe of the meter on point B. The meter reads up scale +12 volts. Point B is 12 volts positive with respect to the reference point (chassis ground — the negative terminal of the battery). Here are the other voltages in the circuit with respect to the reference point (keeping the common (–) probe of the meter on chassis ground):

Point	Meter Reading	Comment
A(A¹)	0V	
C	0V	When ignition switch is OFF
C	+ 12V	When ignition switch is ON
D	0V	
E	0V	When ignition switch is OFF
E	+ 12V	When ignition switch is ON

Figure 3-3. Automotive Starter Circuit

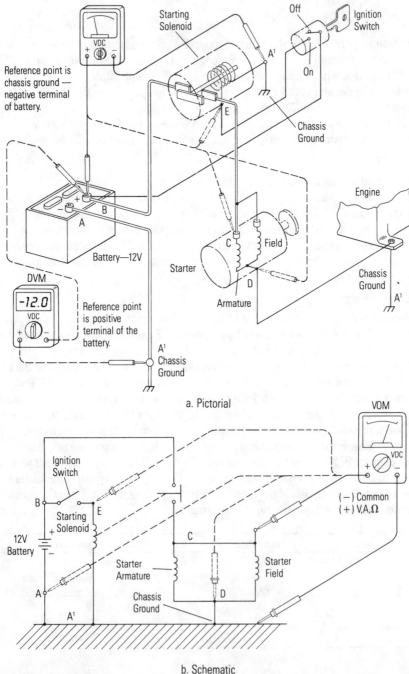

a. Pictorial

b. Schematic

Note that when a voltage measurement is made the meter is across two points. In all cases above, all points are a positive voltage with respect to the reference point, or else they have the same potential as the reference point (the voltage is 0 volts).

Other reference points could have been chosen. *Figure 3-3a* also shows the case when the common probe (–) of a DVM is connected to the + terminal of the battery. Now the measured voltages at the various points (moving the + probe) are:

Point	Meter Reading	Comment
A(A¹)	– 12V	
B	0V	
C	– 12V	When ignition switch is OFF
C	0V	When ignition switch is ON
D	– 12V	
E	– 12V	When ignition switch is OFF
E	0V	When ignition switch is ON

Note that the negative terminal of the battery, which is connected to chassis ground has a polarity of –12 volts, and the polarity of point D is –12V instead of 0 volts when the reference point was the negative terminal of the battery. *So the polarity of a point in the circuit depends on the point chosen for the reference point.*

Polarity of Voltage Drops

One other main point on polarity relates to the polarity of voltage drops across components in a circuit. Refer to *Figure 3-4* where three resistors are in a series circuit with a battery. The voltage drops across the resistors add together to equal the battery voltage. The end of the resistor closest to the positive terminal of the battery will be positive while the end closest to the negative terminal of the battery will be negative.

If a DVM is connected with its common probe at point D, the intersection of R_2 and R_3, then the voltage read across R_2 will be a positive voltage (point A), and the voltage read across $R_1 + R_2$ (point B) will be a positive voltage. However, the voltage read across R3 (point C) will be a negative voltage because of the polarity of the voltage drop across R_3 and the fact that point D is the reference point.

If the common probe of the DVM is moved to point A, it becomes the reference point, and the polarity of voltage readings are:

Point	Voltage Drop
B	V_{R1} is positive
D	V_{R2} is negative
C	V_{R3} is negative

With this review of Ohm's law, series and parallel circuits and polarity, let's move on to look at multitester measurements.

Figure 3-4. Polarity of Voltage Drops

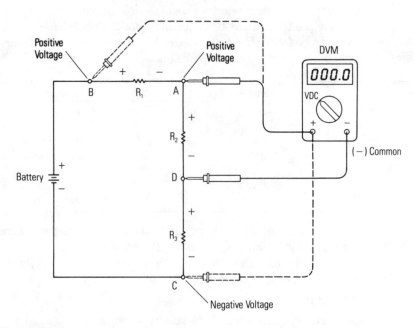

METER LOADING

Meter loading can affect voltage measurements and cause inaccurate readings. The concept of meter loading is explained best by looking at an example illustrated in *Figure 3-5*. In *Figure 3-5a* a VOM is used to measure the voltage across R_2 in a simple dc series circuit which is supplied current by the voltage V. Notice that to make the voltage measurement you must place the voltmeter *across* resistor R_2. The common (–) probe of the meter is at point A and the (+) probe of the meter is at point B. The VOM is represented by a resistor in series with a meter movement. The value of the combination is equal to the input impedance (resistance) of the meter.

Meter Forms Parallel Branch

As shown in the equivalent circuit of *Figure 3-5b*, placing the VOM across R_2 forms a parallel branch of the circuit with R_2. It adds another path through R_M for current besides the path through R_2. It means that I_T increases because now I_T equals I_1 plus I_2 rather than just I_1 without the meter present. How large will I_2 be? As discussed in Chapter 1, if the voltage drop is large enough across R_2 to cause a full scale VOM reading on the meter range chosen, the current I_2 through R_M will be equal to the current required to deflect the meter movement to full scale.

    R_M in parallel with R_2 reduces the equivalent circuit resistance represented by the parallel branch, and produces a corresponding error in the voltage across R_2. Let's demonstrate with actual values.

Figure 3-5. Meter Loading When Making Voltage Measurements

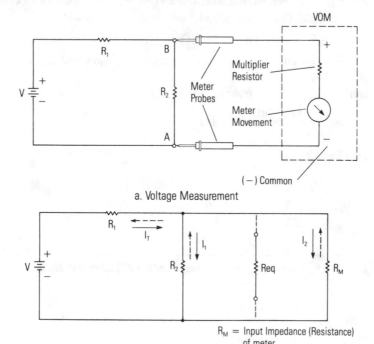

a. Voltage Measurement

R_M = Input Impedance (Resistance) of meter

b. Equivalent Parallel Circuit

Measurement Error

The equivalent resistance of the parallel branch is

$$Req = \frac{R_2 R_M}{R_2 + R_M}$$

Let's assume the normal circuit values are:

$$V = 10V$$
$$R_1 = 1k\Omega$$
$$R_2 = 1k\Omega$$

Without the voltmeter measurement, using Ohm's law the total current I_T and the voltage drops across R_1 and R_2 can be calculated as follows:

$$R_T = 2k\Omega$$

$$I_T = \frac{10V}{2k\Omega} = 5mA$$

$$V_{R1} = 1k\Omega \times 5mA = 5V$$

$$V_{R2} = 1k\Omega \times 5mA = 5V$$

Therefore, if a voltage measurement is made without error, the voltage across R_2 would equal 5 volts.

● *Measuring with a 200 Ohms/Volt Meter*

Suppose a voltage measurement is made using a VOM that has an internal impedance of 200 ohms per volt, and a full scale range of 5 volts is used. As a result,

$$R_M = 5V \times 200 \text{ ohms/v} = 1000 \text{ ohms}$$

Making the voltage measurement with this VOM makes an equivalent circuit like that shown in *Figure 3-6a.*

Req can be calculated from equation above as

$$Req = \frac{1k\Omega \times 1k\Omega}{2k\Omega} = 0.5k\Omega$$

As shown in *Figure 3-6,*

$$R_T = 1.5k\Omega$$
$$I_T = 6.67mA$$
$$V_{R1} = 6.67V$$
$$V_{R2} = 3.33V$$

Figure 3-6. Voltage Across R₂ When Measured with a 200 Ohm/Volt Meter

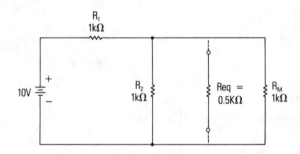

a. Equivalent Circuit

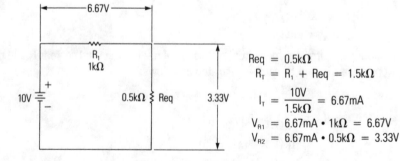

Req = 0.5kΩ
R_T = R₁ + Req = 1.5kΩ

$$I_T = \frac{10V}{1.5k\Omega} = 6.67mA$$

V_{R1} = 6.67mA • 1kΩ = 6.67V
V_{R2} = 6.67mA • 0.5kΩ = 3.33V

b. Voltage Across R₂

The voltage measured across R_2 (which is really Req because of the parallel R_M) is 3.33V, and the percent error in the measurement is

$$\% \text{ Error} = \frac{5.00V - 3.33V}{5.00} \times 100$$

$$\% \text{ Error} = \frac{1.67}{5.00} \times 100$$

$$\% \text{ Error} = 33\%$$

Making the measurement with a 200 ohms/volt meter has caused the measurement to be in error by 33%.

Measuring With 1000, 2000, and 20,000 VOMs, *Table 3-1* lists the circuit values and errors when the measurement is made on the 5 volt scale. The input impedances are 5000, 10,000, and 100,000 ohms.

Table 3-1. Percent Error Due to R_M

VOM Ohm/Volt	VOM R_M	R_2	Req	R_1	R_T	I_T	V_{R1}	V_{REQ} (V_{R2})	% Error
k	k	k	k	k	k	mA	V	V	%
1	5	1	0.883	1	1.833	5.45	5.45	4.55	9.0
2	10	1	0.910	1	1.910	5.24	5.24	4.76	4.8
20	100	1	0.990	1	1.990	5.03	5.03	4.97	0.6

When R_M equals 5 kilohms the voltage measurement is still in error by 9%. Not until a VOM is used that has an internal impedance R_M of 10 kilohms (10 times the value of R_2, the resistance across which the voltage is measured) does the error (4.8%) come down into the range of measurement error of the VOM itself (usually 2% to 4%). *Therefore, to prevent meter loading on a voltage measurement, make sure the input impedance (resistance) of the voltmeter used for measurement is at least 10 times the impedance (resistance) across which the measurement is made.*

Accuracy Compromise

The value of R_M, the VOM input impedance, increases as the voltage full-scale range is increased. A 1000 ohm per volt meter will have an $R_M = 10,000$ ohms on the 10 volt scale and an $R_M = 50,000$ ohms on the 50 volt scale. To have R_M large so it does not load the circuit, the full-scale range should be large so the loading error is small. However, to have the greatest reading accuracy, the full-scale range should be as small as possible to make the meter deflection as close to full scale as possible. These are contradictory statements, so the choice of which full-scale range to use is a compromise when the loading of R_M is going to cause significant error.

Measurement with a DVM

As explained in Chapter 2, electronic circuitry is used in a digital voltmeter. As a result, the input impedance is quite high, usually 1 megohm (one million ohms). Therefore, normal voltage measurements across components that have as high a resistance value as 100,000 ohms will have little or no error. This is one of the significant advantages of using a DVM, little circuit loading occurs unless resistances approach megohm values.

BASIC DC MEASUREMENTS

A typical VOM is shown in *Figure 3-7*. It is an instrument that is easy to use and simple to operate; therefore, it is very popular with the handyman or the beginner in electricity and electronics. It functions as a voltmeter, ammeter, or ohmmeter depending on the position of a selector switch.

It has 43 ranges — 12 for dc voltage from 0 - 1000 volts, 8 for ac voltages from 0 - 1000 volts, 10 for dc current up to a maximum of 10 amperes, and 5 resistance ranges to measure resistance from 0 to 20 megohms (20×10^{-6} ohms). A special switch doubles the number of ranges on dc voltage and current and ac voltage by cutting the full-scale of each range in half to provide extra resolution and higher accuracy in the reading. The sensitivity of this meter is 50,000 ohms per volt. That means that the meter movement deflects to full scale with just 20 microamperes (0.00002A) of current.

Making a VOM DC Voltage Measurement

To make a voltage measurement follow these steps. The voltage to be measured is the voltage across R_3 in *Figure 3-8*.

1. To prevent an error being introduced, the zero of the meter should be checked before any measurement is made. With a VOM, the instrument should be off and the pointer zero position adjusted mechanically with the zero adjust screw as described in the instrument manual.

Figure 3-7. VOM

2. Set the range selector switch to the dc voltage range desired. It usually is best to start with a range greater than the final one. If you do not know the approximate value of the voltage, place the selector switch on the highest range.

3. Turn on power. Place the minus (–) meter probe at point A. Now touch the plus (+) probe momentarily to point B. Watch the meter needle and see if it moves up scale. If no movement is detected, rotate the range switch to the next lowest scale until a deflection is noted.

4. If the deflection is up scale, hold the plus probe to point B permanently. (If your test probes have clips on them, clip the leads in place.)

5. If the deflection is down scale (below zero) reverse the leads or, if the meter has a +/– polarity switch, switch the polarity so that the deflection is up scale.

6. Rotate the selector switch to get the greatest on-scale needle deflection without exceeding full scale. In the example of *Figure 3-8*, the voltage is 4 volts; therefore, the selector switch would be set on 10 volts and the meter would read 4 on the 10 volts scale as shown in *Figure 3-8b*. The 2.5 volt scale of the VOM of *Figure 3-7* would cause the meter to go beyond full scale.

7. The meter of *Figure 3-7* has a switch that reduces the range selected in half. Switching the switch to V/2 reduces the full-scale range to 5 volts and the needle would now read 4 volts as shown in the dotted line position of *Figure 3-8b*. (The actual reading is taken using the 50 volt scale and, because the range selector is on the 5 volt range, every meter reading is divided by 10.) This provides a deflection closer to full scale, and thus, a more accurate reading.

8. Parallax is reduced by aligning the needle with the image in the mirror above the dc voltage scales.

9. If the battery voltage is to be measured, the plus probe would be momentarily touched to point C of *Figure 3-8a* with the range selector switch on the 50 volt range. Steps 4 through 8 would then be followed to read 12 volts on the 25 volt range.

Figure 3-8. DC Voltage Measurement

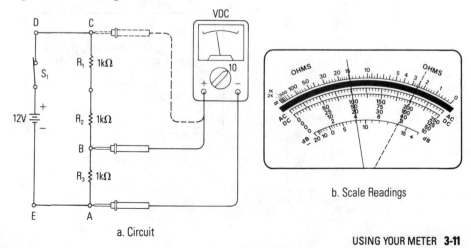

a. Circuit

b. Scale Readings

Making a VOM DC Current Measurement

Current measurements are different. The meter must be inserted into the circuit so that the circuit current is through the ammeter. *Figure 3-9* shows a VOM used as an ammeter inserted in the series circuit of *Figure 3-8* to measure the series circuit current. The steps to be followed for this measurement are as follows:

1. With the meter out of the circuit, check the zero position of the meter and mechanically adjust it with the zero adjust screw if required.
2. Turn off the circuit power and disconnect the circuit so that the meter may be inserted. In *Figure 3-9*, point C is disconnected from the battery terminal at point D and the ammeter inserted.
3. Set the range selector switch to the highest dc current range. Some VOMs will have a function switch so that volts or amperes or ohms may have to be selected as well as the range. If so, the amperes function would be selected.
4. Place the plus probe of the meter at the most positive voltage point (point D) and the minus probe at the more negative voltage point (point C). The direction of current is as shown.
5. Turn on power. Touch the terminal C momentarily to see that the meter needle deflects up scale when power is on. If deflection is down scale, reverse the meter leads.

Figure 3-9. DC Current Measurement

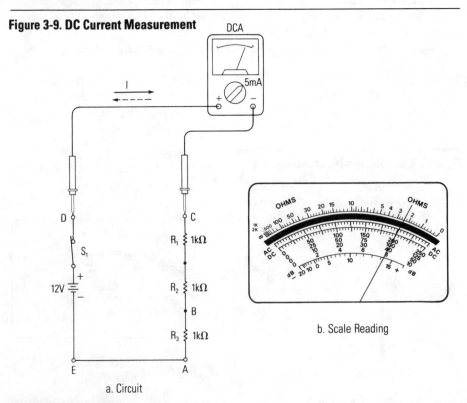

a. Circuit

b. Scale Reading

6. After power is on, adjust the selector switch to give the greatest on-scale deflection. Since the current in *Figure 3-9* is 4 milliamperes, the range selector would be set on 5 milliampers full scale, and the needle would read 4 milliamperes as shown in *Figure 3-9b* (as with the voltage measurement, the 50 scale is used and all readings divided by 10). There is no need to use the half-scale function switch in this case.

Be aware that the highest current range is 10 amperes. However, the plus (+) lead must be plugged into an auxiliary jack to activate the 10A current range.

Making a VOM Resistance Measurement

Complete information on the condition of electrical circuits and the circuit components cannot be obtained by the use of the voltmeter and the ammeter alone. Using an ohmmeter adds significantly to your information about a circuit. Knowing for sure that a circuit is complete (there is continuity) and being able to measure the resistance of the various circuit components are valuable pieces of circuit information obtained by using an ohmmeter.

Recall that a VOM when used as an ohmmeter supplies its own current from an internal power source (either 1 or 2 batteries) to operate the meter movement. All circuit power is to be turned off or removed when making continuity and resistance measurements, otherwise there is danger of damaging or completely burning out the VOM.

● *Example Measurement*

The meter of *Figure 3-7* uses a series circuit for the ohmmeter. As a result, zero on the resistance scale is full-scale deflection, and open circuit or "infinity" ohms is the idle position of the needle. We will measure the resistance of the circuit of *Figure 3-8* as shown in *Figure 3-10*. Follow these steps:

1. Make sure power is disconnected from the circuit.
2. Make sure the VOM is on the ohmmeter function, either by the position of the range selector switch or by a function switch that selects the ohmmeter function or both.
3. Short the meter leads together and with the OHMS (Ω) ADJUST control, adjust the meter reading to 0 ohms. If this adjustment cannot be made, the battery internal in the meter needs to be replaced.
4. Place the meter leads across the resistance to be measured. For example, point A and point C in *Figure 3-10*.
5. Change the range selector switch to cause the meter reading to be between half-scale and full-scale if possible, or as close to half-scale as possible. If the meter reading is close to the high resistance end of the scale, select a higher resistance range; if the reading is closer to the low resistance end, select a lower resistance range. Of course with very high resistances, the meter reading will always be to the left (high resistance end) of the scale.

Figure 3-10. Resistance Measurement

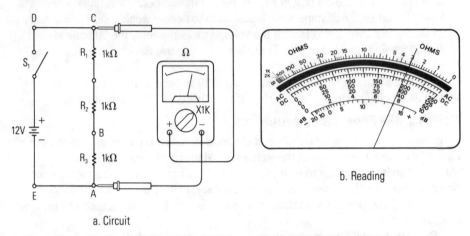

a. Circuit

b. Reading

6. Since the resistance in this case is 3 kilohms, the range selector would end up on the R × 1K range and the meter would read 3 as shown in *Figure 3-10b*. The range switch selects different values that multiply the meter reading. On the R × 1 scale, the meter reading is taken directly. On the R × 10K all readings are multipled by 10,000.

When making in-circuit measurements, remember that circuit paths in parallel with the component being measured may cause reading errors. Check the circuit diagram for the presence of such parallel paths before assuming that the reading obtained is correct.

● *VOM Resistance Measurement Accuracy*

The accuracy of a VOM in making resistance measurements is slightly different from its accuracy in making voltage and current measurements. The percent of accuracy of an ohmmeter at center scale is specified as a percentage of the complete arc made by the needle when reading resistances from 0 to infinity. A typical accuracy is 2% of arc. To maintain this accuracy, it is most important that the idle position of the needle be set on the end of scale mark with the mechanical screw adjustment and that the full-scale adjustment be set on the end of scale mark with the OHMS ADJUST control.

DVM DC Voltage Measurements

A digital multimeter like the one shown in *Figure 3-11* is chosen for our example measurements. Two significant differences are apparent between this DVM and a VOM. First, the output is a digital display where the meter reading is a particular number. Second, since electronic circuits are required to produce the conversion required, power must be supplied to the electronic circuits; therefore, the DVM has a power switch which must be ON for all measurements.

As shown in *Figure 3-11*, beyond these differences, functionally the DVM and VOM are very similar. Selector switches select the function and the range, the meter leads are plugged into a common (–) jack and a plus (+) jack to make measurements, or the plus lead is plugged into a special auxiliary jack for a special current range of 10A.

Figure 3-11. DVM Used for Example Measurements

The steps for making a voltage measurement with a DVM using the circuit of *Figure 3-8* are basically the same as they are when a VOM is used. The exceptions are that no zero adjustments or polarity precautions are necessary because the meter takes care of these automatically. The actual reading will be a number on the digital display. For example, the four volt measurements of *Figure 3-8* would read 4.00 on the 30 volt range, if it is exactly four volts; otherwise, it will read some fractional voltage to two decimal places.

● *Polarity*

Test leads need not be switched when measuring with a DVM. The display will indicate whether the voltage reading is a positive or negative voltage with respect to the common lead.

● *Overrange and Fused Protection*

A special indicator also appears on the display to indicate that the reading is over range on the range selected. Change the range selector to the next highest range until a digital reading is obtained or the highest range is reached. The voltage being measured exceeds the highest full-scale reading if an overrange indication is obtained on the highest range. Many instruments also are fused against excessive current on any range.

● *Low Battery Voltage*

A special indicator usually is available to indicate when the internal batteries supplying power must be replaced.

DVM DC Current Measurements

The current measurement functionally is the same as the steps outlined for the VOM current measurement, except, as for the voltage measurements, the leads need not be exchanged from wrong polarity, and there is no zero adjustment. The 4 milliamperes would read 4.00 on the 30 milliamperes range, if it is exactly four milliamperes; otherwise, some fractional value to two decimal places will be indicated.

As explained in Chapter 2, what is actually happening in the current measurement is that a small resistance is inserted in the circuit and the DVM is measuring the small voltage drop across the resistance due to the circuit current.

DVM Resistance Measurements

The same precautions must be followed when measuring resistance with a DVM as with a VOM. Remove power from the circuit before making resistance measurement. The measurement is made with the test leads across the component to be measured. Current from the DVM causes a voltage drop across the component resistance and the voltage is read by the DVM and converted to a direct resistance measurement.

When measuring the resistance of *Figure 3-10*, the DVM would read 3.00 on the 30 kilohm range if the resistance is exactly 3000 ohms; otherwise, the reading would be some fractional value to two decimal places.

BASIC AC MEASUREMENTS

Here are some factors that are important when making ac measurements.

1. AC voltage and current measurements depend on frequency. Consult the meter manual to determine the limits of the meter's frequency response.
2. Most VOMs read in rms values, but ac meters can either read average, rms, or true rms values. Only true rms reading meters do not require the ac signal to be a sine wave without producing error.
3. AC current measurements are accomplished by rectifying a voltage developed across a resistor in the circuit.
4. AC VOM readings are accurate to a percent of full-scale, but the accuracy and sensitivity are usually less than for dc measurements.
5. Non-linear rectifier characteristics make small ac voltage measurements less accurate.
6. VOMs usually have more loading effect on the circuit than for dc.
7. On ac measurements, a DVM usually has the same accuracy, sensitivity and circuit loading as it does on dc.
8. When an ac voltage is applied to circuits that only have resistance (such as *Figures 3-8* and *3-9*), the measurement steps are the same as outlined for dc measurements. There will be no polarity observance needed because the ac voltage or current is alternating positive and negative with time.

Clamp-On Current Meters

Some VOMs today have a clamp-on accessory that may be used as a clamp-on ammeter for measuring ac currents. This adapter is clamped around a wire carrying a large ac current and the current is then transformed to an ac voltage so that the VOM uses the ac volts function to measure the ac current in the conductor. There may be special scales included on the meter face for the clamp-on adapter so the current can be read directly.

AC Impedance and Reactance

The opposition to current in a dc circuit is termed resistance. If the opposition to current in an ac circuit is due to resistance, the effect is the same; however, if the circuit contains inductors or capacitors, the opposition to ac current is more complex. As discussed previously, inductors are coils of wire wound around iron cores contained in motors, generators, solenoids, relays, chokes, and transformers. Capacitors are the components that store charge on parallel plates separated by a dielectric so there is no dc path through the capacitor. Inductors store energy in magnetic fields; capacitors store energy in electrostatic fields.

Reactance

The opposition offered by an inductor or capacitor is called reactance. The reactance of each of the components is frequency sensitive. Inductive reactance is expressed as

$$X_L = 2\pi fL$$

and capacitive reactance is expressed as

$$X_C = \frac{1}{2\pi fC}$$

where f is frequency in hertz (cycles per second), L is inductance in henries, C is capacitance in farads, and π is a constant 3.1416 --- .

The unit for reactance is ohms just like resistance. If $f = 0$ (which is dc), X_L will be zero and X_C will be infinity. If $f = \infty$ (infinity), X_L will be equal to infinity and X_C will be zero.

● Impedance

Impedance is the term given to the total opposition to ac current when both resistance and reactance are present to impede the current. The reactance can be inductive, capacitive or a combination of both. What makes impedance and ac voltage and current complex is that measured quantities do not add directly. They must be added vectorially.

● Vector Addition

How voltage, current and impedance add vectorially is best demonstrated by an example. Look at *Figure 3-12*. A 60 cycle 50 volt (rms voltages are identified by VAC) power source is connected to a resistor and solenoid. The resistor has 30 ohms resistance, and the solenoid has 40 ohms inductive reactance. To find the total impedance of the circuit the resistance and reactance must be combined at right angles as shown in *Figure 3-12*. The resistance is plotted horizontally and the reactance is plotted 90° upright from it, joined tip to tail and represented by arrows called vectors with appropriate length and to the same scale. The total impedance Z is another vector from the start (tail) of the resistance to the tip of the reactance. This forms the hypotenuse (the long side) of a right triangle.

Figure 3-12. Impedance with R and X$_L$

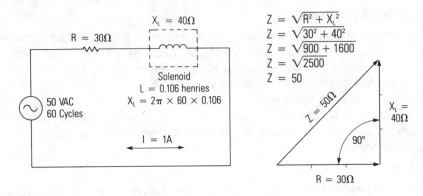

A mathematical theorem (Pythagorean's Theorem) states that the hypotenuse of a right triangle is equal to the square root of the sum of the squares of the sides. Therefore, the total impedance of the circuit of *Figure 3-12* can be calculated as

$$Z = \sqrt{30^2 + 40^2}$$
$$Z = \sqrt{900 + 1600}$$
$$Z = \sqrt{2500}$$
$$Z = 50$$

Since Z is the total opposition, the total current in this series circuit can be found by using a form of Ohm's law for ac circuits:

$$I = \frac{V}{Z}$$

or

$$I = \frac{50V}{50\Omega}$$
$$I = 1A$$

The total current is one ampere.

Ohm's law for ac circuits can now be used to find the voltage across the respective components. The voltage across the resistance is

$$V_R = I \times R$$
$$V_R = 1A \times 30\Omega$$
$$V_R = 30V$$

The voltage across the inductance is

$$V_L = I \times X_L$$
$$V_L = 1A \times 40\Omega$$
$$V_L = 40V$$

Voltage Measurements

If a VOM on an ac voltage range of 50 volts is used to measure the voltage across the resistance and inductance, the voltages measured would be 30 volts across the resistance and 40 volts across the solenoid. If now the source voltage is measured, it would measure 50 volts. Each of these measurements is shown in *Figure 3-13*. Note that the voltages across each of the components add directly to 70 volts, but the source voltage is only 50 volts. *In circuits where the total impedance is made up of resistance and reactance, the measured voltages must be added vectorially. Figure 3-13* shows how the total voltage of 50 volts is the vectorial sum of the 30 volts across the resistance and 40 volts across the solenoid.

The steps for making the voltage measurements are basically the same as for dc. Summarized they are:

1. With leads open, adjust the zero reading of the meter with the mechanical zero adjust, if available.
2. Set the function selector switch to the highest ac voltage range.
3. Measure voltage; adjust voltage range downward to get a meter reading as close to full-scale as possible.

Figure 3-13. Voltage Measurements of *Figure 3-12* Circuit

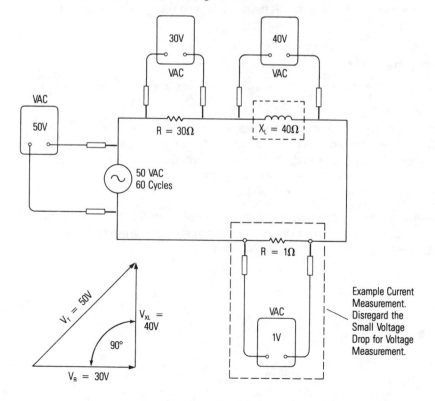

Current Measurements

Current measurements are made in ac circuits by using the current function on the selector switch and inserting the meter leads into the circuit just as with dc current measurements. If your meter does not have an ac current function, current measurements can be made easily by inserting a small known value of resistance into the circuit and measuring the ac voltage across it. An example is shown in the dotted insert of *Figure 3-13*. The voltage drop across the one ohm resistor used for the current measurements may be disregarded when the voltage measurements are made.

Caution: *When making current measurements in ac circuits that contain parallel branches with inductors and capacitors in parallel, very high circulating currents can be encountered in the parallel branches at particular frequencies of the applied voltage.*

Impedance Measurements

Even though there are special impedance meters where meter scales are calibrated in ohms impedance, VOMs and DVMs normally do not have impedance scales as they have resistance scales. Impedances are obtained by measuring voltage and current and calculating impedance.

POWER MEASUREMENTS AND CALCULATIONS

Indirect measurement of voltage and current will provide the power being delivered or dissipated in a circuit. The power P, using a measured voltage V, and current I is calculated as

$$P = I \times V$$

DC Circuits

In dc circuits the power calculation is a direct one. The power is dissipated as heat.

AC Circuits

In ac circuits, reactance again complicates the power calculation. The multiplication of voltage times current may not result in true dissipated power, but may result in an "apparent" power because of the reactances present. Consult a more detailed text on ac circuits for a more complete understanding of the subject.

SUMMARY

With the description of the meters and how they operate and a basic understanding of measurements, we move on in the next chapter to some actual practical examples of meter measurements.

MEASUREMENT OF INDIVIDUAL COMPONENTS

An important part of the field of electronics is understanding the various components and electron devices that make up complex electronic circuits. Every electrical circuit has three inherent properties: resistance, capacitance and inductance. Measuring common components with these properties using a multimeter is the subject of this chapter.

HOW TO MEASURE A RESISTOR

Resistor Basics — Fixed and Variable

Resistance in a circuit is the opposition to current. All materials used in an electric circuit will offer some resistance. Those offering low resistance are called conductors and are used as paths for current. Those offering extremely high resistance provide no path for current and are called insulators. Components manufactured specifically to be placed in a circuit to provide resistance are called resistors and are used most frequently in electrical circuits to limit current or to create voltage drops. Insulators are used to resist or prevent current in certain paths.

Resistors come in different values, shapes and sizes. Resistors are classified two ways — by resistance measured in ohms and by power rating measured in watts. The power rating of resistors for electronic circuits range from 1/8 watt to hundreds of watts. The ohmic values range from hundredths of ohms (0.01) to hundreds of megohms (100 x 10^6). Manufacturers have adopted a standard color code system for indicating the resistance or ohmic value of low power resistors (normally below 2 watts). Higher power resistors usually have the resistance value imprinted on their bodies. An assortment of different types of resistors with different wattage ratings are shown in *Figure 4-1.*

Figure 4-1. Different Type Resistors

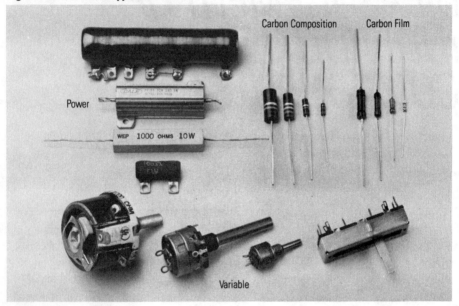

Construction

The small wattage rating resistors (also physically small) are usually carbon composition or deposited carbon. The carbon composition resistors are made of finely ground carbon mixed with a binder molded to a shape with pigtail leads. The compressed mixture can be made to have a resistance from one ohm to tens of megohms. This type resistor usually has wattage ratings of 2 watts or less, and the resistance value is indicated by color coded bands encircling the body of the resistor. The deposited carbon resistor consists of carbon vapor deposited on a glass or ceramic form. Spiral paths are etched into the carbon until the desired resistance is obtained. Such resistors are usually higher precision types (value is accurate to 1% or less).

Wirewound resistors of different wattage ratings also are shown in *Figure 4-1*. They are made of resistance wire wound on a ceramic core. Fusible resistors are a special type of wirewound resistor made to burn out and open the circuit to protect other components if current becomes greater than the fuse resistor is designed to handle.

Figure 4-1 also shows two types of variable resistors. A variable resistor is either carbon or wirewound with a movable wiper arm that will contact the resistance element at any point between the end extremes. When the arm is moved, usually with a shaft, the resistance between the wiper arm and either end varies. These variable resistors are commonly called potentiometers or rheostats. If three terminals are used in the circuit, it is referred to as a potentiometer. If only two terminals are used, it is referred to as a rheostat.

Color Codes

Resistor values are measured in ohms with an ohmmeter. As shown in *Figure 4-2*, a common way of indicating resistance values for composition resistors is to use color bands on the body of the resistor. A standard color code for the bands has been adopted by resistor manufacturers, and the numerical values they represent are given in *Table 4-1*. *Figure 4-2* shows how to evaluate the bands. The first band will be nearer one end of the resistor. Read from this band toward the other end. The first band is the first significant number; the second band, the second significant number; and the third band, the multiplier (number of zeros that follow the first two numbers) to indicate the resistor's value. If the third band is gold or silver, this would indicate a multiplier of 0.1 or 0.01, respectively, rather than additional zeros.

As the resistors are manufactured they all will not be exactly the same value. The fourth band indicates the tolerance of the resistor's value from the indicated (color code) value. A gold fourth band indicates ±5%, a silver band ±10%, and no fourth band indicates a tolerance of ±20%. The resistor's value will be within a tolerance band of ±5%, ±10%, or ±20% of the color coded value.

The resistor in *Figure 4-2* is a 27,000 ohm or 27 kilohm resistor with a ±10% tolerance. The value of the resistor can be anywhere from 24,300 ohms to 29,700 ohms. As shown in *Figure 4-1*, its physical size indicates the power rating.

Figure 4-2. Color Bands Indicating Resistance

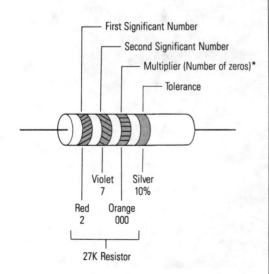

Table 4-1. Resistor Color Code

Color	Value
Black	0
Brown	1
Red	2
Orange	3
Yellow	4
Green	5
Blue	6
Violet	7
Gray	8
White	9

Tolerance	
Gold	5%
Silver	10%
No Band	20%

*If multiplier band is gold, the multiplier is 0.1; if it is silver, the multiplier is 0.01.

Measuring a Fixed Resistor

● *Out of Circuit*

One of the easiest measurements to make with a VOM is to measure the value of a fixed resistor out of a circuit. Use the VOM as an ohmmeter and connect the test leads of the ohmmeter across the resistor as shown in *Figure 4-3*.

● *In Circuit*

Recall from Chapter 1 the two precautions that must be observed when using an ohmmeter to measure a resistance in a circuit:

1. The power source must be turned off. Disconnect the equipment from the power source, if possible.
2. When the resistor is in a circuit, if possible, disconnect one end of the resistor from any circuit or additional component so only the resistance of the single resistor is measured.

Figure 4-4 shows the correct way to measure the resistance of R_3. Notice the supply Vs has been disconnected. Also, note that one end of R_3 is disconnected from the circuit so the ohmmeter measures the resistance of R_3 alone. If R_3 is not disconnected, then the value of resistance measured would be R_3 in parallel with R_2.

Figure 4-3. Measuring a Resistor Out of a Circuit

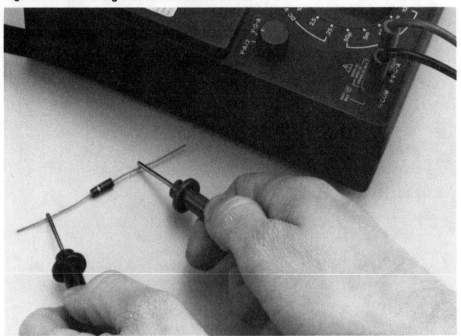

Figure 4-4. Measuring a Resistor in a Circuit

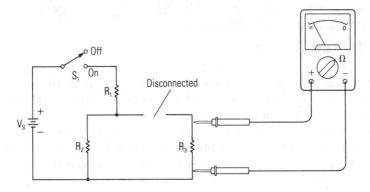

Measuring a Variable Resistor

When a potentiometer is checked with an ohmmeter, the total resistance is first measured from end-to-end as shown for point A in *Figure 4-5*. The reading typically may be within a tolerance of ± 20% of the stated value. Next, the resistance should be tested from the wiper arm to one end as the potentiometer is rotated through its full range as shown for Point B in *Figure 4-5*. The resistance should vary smoothly from near zero to the full value of the resistance. Since the reading should vary smoothly and continuously, this is one place where a VOM has the edge on the DVM. Any sudden jump to either a higher or lower value, or any erratic reading would indicate a defective spot on the resistance element. If the wiper arm is not making firm contact with the resistance element, simply tapping the case of the potentiometer may produce erratic resistance readings. Any of these erratic indications mean a defective or dirty potentiometer. A spray cleaner may salvage the unit; however, if after cleaning it does not produce a smooth resistance change over its entire range, it should be discarded.

Figure 4-5. Measuring a Variable Resistor

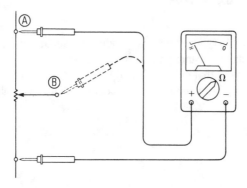

Rheostats may be tested by a similar process with the exception that the only measurement is from the wiper to one end since the rheostat only has two terminals. In general, rheostats will be open if they are defective because they usually are high wattage units and must handle high current.

Thermally Intermittent Resistors

All electronic components, including fixed and variable resistors, can be thermally intermittent. Measure the resistance while subjecting the suspected component to extreme temperature change to detect this type of defect. Radio Shack stores stock an aerosol spray component cooler to spray on a resistor to cool it. The tip of the soldering iron can be used to heat it. Be careful not to apply such an excessive heat to damage the resistor. A sudden or erratic change in resistance as temperature is changed indicates the resistor is thermally intermittent and defective.

"Shifty" Resistors

There is a class of resistors whose resistances change as the operating conditions change. Common ones are thermistors, varistors, and photoconductors. Thermistors and photoconductors can be measured with an ohmmeter. The resistance of a varistor is calculated from voltage and current measurements.

● Thermistors

A thermistor is a resistor whose resistance varies with temperature. It exhibits large negative temperature characteristics; that is, the resistance decreases as the temperature rises and increases as the temperature falls.

● Varistors

A varistor is a resistor whose resistance is voltage dependent. Its resistance decreases as voltage across it is increased.

● Photoconductors

A photo cell's resistance (photoconductor) varies when light shines on it. When the cell is not illuminated, its "dark" resistance may be greater than 100 kilohms. When illuminated, the cell resistance may fall to a few hundred ohms. These values can be measured with an ohmmeter.

HOW TO MEASURE A CAPACITOR

Capacitor Basics

Capacitance is the property whereby two conductors separated by a non-conductor (dielectric material) have the ability to store energy in the form of an electric charge and oppose any change in that charge. The operation of a capacitor depends on the electrostatic field set up between the two oppositely charged parallel plates.

The unit of capacity is the farad, named in honor of Michael Faraday. It is the amount of capacitance which will cause a capacitor to attain a charge of one coulomb when one volt is applied. Expressed as a mathematical equation:

$$C = \frac{Q}{V}$$

where C will be one farad when Q is one coulomb and V is one volt.

The value of capacitance, the farad, is very large for practical applications; therefore, smaller values are used. A microfarad is 10^{-6} farads; a nanofarad is 10^{-9} farads; and a picofarad is 10^{-12} farads. Microfarads and picofarads are very common in electronic circuits.

The physical factors which determine the amount of capacitance a capacitor offers to a circuit are:

a. the type of dielectric material, (K);
b. the area in square meters of the plates, (A);
c. the number of plates, (n); and
d. the spacing of the plates in meters, which also is the thickness of the dielectric, (t).

The basic capacitor and its symbol are shown in *Figure 4-6* with the relationship between the physical factors indicated so the amount of capacitance can be calculated. n = 6 in *Figure 4-6b*, but the most common capacitors have 2 parallel plates.

Caution: Before a capacitor is measured with an ohmmeter, remove it from the circuit and short across its leads or plates to make sure it has no residual charge. Such residual charge could damage an ohmmeter.

Figure 4-6. Basic Parallel Plate Capacitor

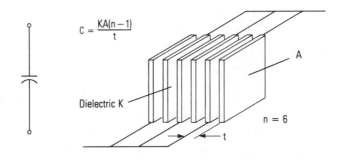

$$C = \frac{KA(n-1)}{t}$$

Dielectric K

A

n = 6

t

a. Symbol   b. Parallel Plate Capacitor (6 plates)

Relative Amount of Capacitance

Two capacitors can be compared as to their relative capacitance by using a VOM. The amount of needle deflection of an ohmmeter can be used to indicate a relative amount of capacitance. By connecting the ohmmeter to the capacitor as shown in *Figure 4-7a*, the ohmmeter battery charges the capacitor to its voltage. The meter will deflect initially and then fall back to infinity as the capacitor charges. In *Figure 4-7b*, after the initial charge of the capacitor, the ohmmeter leads are reversed and the capacitor voltage is now in series with the voltage inside the ohmmeter. The charge on the capacitor is aiding the ohmmeter battery. The needle now deflects a larger deflection proportionally to the amount of capacitance, and then decays as the charge is redistributed on the capacitor.

Leaky and Shorted Capacitors

Paper, mica and ceramic capacitors fail in two ways. The dielectric breaks down and the capacitor plates short together, or the capacitor becomes "leaky." When "leaky," the dielectric still supports a voltage but the dielectric resistance becomes much lower than normal. Both of these conditions can be detected with a VOM or DVM. There are two checks that can be made. The first is simply a resistance measurement using the VOM or DVM as an ohmmeter across the terminals of the capacitor. If the capacitor is shorted, the ohmmeter will read zero or a very low value of resistance. If the capacitor has become "leaky," then the resistance measurement will be much less than the normal nearly infinite reading for a good capacitor. Leaky capacitors need to be replaced before they turn into shorted capacitors.

Figure 4-7. Measuring Relative Amount of Capacitance

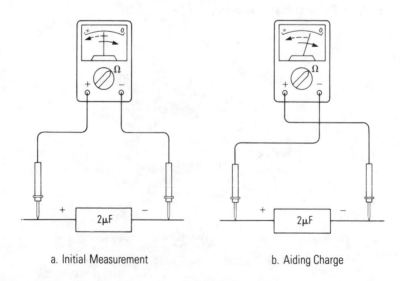

a. Initial Measurement   b. Aiding Charge

In some capacitors, the dielectric does not become "leaky" until a voltage is applied. That is, it breaks down under load. This defect cannot be detected with an ohmmeter but can be found by using the VOM or DVM as a voltmeter as shown in *Figure 4-8*. A dc voltage is placed across the series combination of the voltmeter and the paper, mica, or ceramic capacitor (not for electrolytic capacitors unless proper polarity is maintained). A good capacitor will show only a momentary deflection on the voltmeter, then the reading will decay to zero volts as the capacitor charges to the supply voltage. A defective capacitor will have a low insulation resistance, R_{INS}, (it may be at a particular voltage), and will maintain a voltage reading on the meter. The lower the insulation resistance of the capacitor, the higher the voltmeter will read. When insulation resistance is checked by this method, it is in series with the meter. Because R_{INS} is normally high, it limits the current; therefore, a change in the VOM voltmeter range does not significantly affect the total resistance of the circuit, and the percentage of meter-scale deflection remains fairly constant with different voltmeter ranges. The power supply voltage V_s should be set for the rated working voltage of the capacitor for this test.

If the insulation resistance is such that it produces a scale reading on a VOM or DVM, the R_{INS} may be calculated by using the following equation:

$$R_{INS} = R_{INPUT} \frac{V_S - V_M}{V_M}$$

where V_S = supply voltage
V_M = VOM or DVM measured voltage
R_{INPUT} = VOM or DVM input resistance
R_{INS} = capacitor insulation resistance

Figure 4-8. Measuring R_{INS} Using a Voltmeter

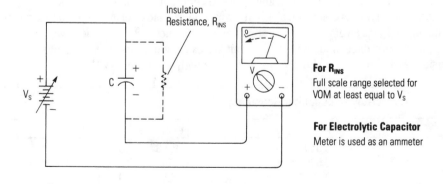

Insulation Resistance, R_{INS}

For R_{INS}
Full scale range selected for VOM at least equal to V_S

For Electrolytic Capacitor
Meter is used as an ammeter

Measuring An Electrolytic Capacitor

Special care must be taken when measuring electrolytic capacitors because they are polarized. As a result, when using a VOM as an ohmmeter to test an electrolytic capacitor, the ohmmeter test lead polarity must be correct to give the proper indication. In most cases, this occurs when the positive ohmmeter test lead is connected to the positive electrolytic capacitor terminal. In any case, the test lead arrangement that gives the highest resistance reading is the one to use.

Leakage Current of Electrolytic Capacitors

Measuring the leakage current of an electrolytic capacitor is the best way to judge whether the capacitor is still useful. The same circuit of *Figure 4-8* is used for measuring leakage current of electrolytic capacitors except now the meter is an ammeter. V_s, the capacitor's rated voltage, is applied across the capacitor, and the leakage current is indicated by the series ammeter. The maximum permissible leakage current of a new electrolytic capactor is related to the voltage rating (WVDC) and capacitance of the capacitor according to the following equation:

$$I = kC + 0.30$$

where
- I = leakage current in ma
- C = rated value of capacitor in microfarads
- k = a constant as given in *Table 4-2*

Many factors affect the amount of leakage, such as, the age of the capacitor, how long it has been uncharged in a circuit, how near its rated voltage it has been working or how long a new one has been on the shelf. If the capacitor exceeds the permissible leakage values, it should be discarded. Experience will help make this test more conclusive.

HOW TO MEASURE INDUCTORS

The property of an electric circuit or component that opposes changes in circuit current is called inductance. The ability of the circuit or component to oppose changes in current is due to its ability to store and release energy that it has stored in a magnetic field. Every circuit has some inherent inductance but devices which purposely introduce inductance to a circuit are called inductors. Let's look at some basics of inductance, and how to test inductors with a VOM or DVM.

Table 4-2. Electrolytic Capacitor Constant k

k	WVDC, volts
0.010	3 — 100
0.020	101 — 250
0.025	251 — 350
0.040	351 — 500

Inductor Basics — Inductance and Impedance

An inductor may take on any number of physical forms and shapes. However, it is basically nothing more than a coil of wire. Inductors are sometimes referred to by such names as choke, impedance coil, reactor, or combinations such as choke coil or inductive reactor. The amount of inductance of a coil is measured by a unit called the henry. Smaller units, like for capacitors, are practical — the millihenry (1×10^{-3} henries) and microhenry (1×10^{-6} henries) are very common units in electronic circuits.

The amount of inductance in an inductor depends on the magnetic flux produced and the current in the coil. Mathematically, this may be expressed by the following equation:

$$L = \frac{N\phi}{I}$$

where   L is the inductance in henries
I is the current through the coil in amperes
N is the number of turns of wire
ϕ is the magnetic flux linking the turns.

Basically all inductors are made by winding a length of conductor around a core which is made either of magnetic material or of insulated material. When a magnetic core is not used, the inductor is said to have an air core. The physical characteristics, or geometry, of both the core and the windings around the core affect the amount of inductance produced. *Figure 4-9* illustrates these factors. The more turns, the better the magnetic core material, the larger core cross section area, and the shorter the coil length all increase the inductance.

In a dc circuit, the only changes in current occur when the circuit is closed to start current, and when it is opened to stop current. However, in an ac circuit, the current is continually changing each time the voltage alternates. Since inductance in a circuit opposes a change in current and ac is continually changing, there is an opposition offered by the inductor to the ac current that is called reactance. The amount of inductive reactance is given by the following equation:

$$X_L = 2\pi fL$$

where X_L is the inductive reactance in ohms,
f is the frequency of the ac in hertz,
L is the inductance in henries.

The quantity $2\pi f$ represents the rate of change of current in radians per second. It is called angular velocity.

In ac circuits that contain only inductance, the inductive reactance is the only thing that limits the current. The current is determined by Ohm's law with X_L replacing R, as follows:

$$I = \frac{V}{X_L}$$

If an ac circuit contains both resistance and inductance (reactance), then the total opposition to current flow is termed impedance and is designated by the letter Z. When a voltage V is applied to a circuit that has an impedance Z, the current I is

$$I = \frac{V}{Z} \left(\text{where } Z = \sqrt{R^2 + X_L{}^2} \right)$$

Continuity

A series RL circuit may be formed by one or more resistors connected in series with one or more coils. Or, since the wire used in any coil has some resistance, a series RL circuit may consist of just a coil or coils by themselves. The resistance of the coils, which effectively is in series with the inductance, supplies the circuit resistance. Using a VOM as an ohmmeter, a simple continuity test will quickly locate an open inductor. The resistance can be measured easily for any inductance that is not open. Just place the meter used as an ohmmeter across the coil terminals and

Figure 4-9. Physical Factors That Affect the Value of Inductance

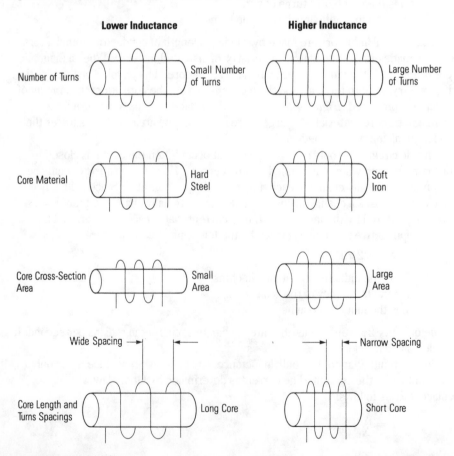

Lower Inductance	Higher Inductance
Number of Turns — Small Number of Turns	Large Number of Turns
Core Material — Hard Steel	Soft Iron
Core Cross-Section Area — Small Area	Large Area
Core Length and Turns Spacings — Wide Spacing — Long Core	Narrow Spacing — Short Core

measure the resistance just like a resistor was measured in *Figure 4-3*. Normal resistance values depend on the wire size and number of turns (length) of the wire that makes up the inductor. Some coils with fine wire and a large number of turns will have hundreds of ohms resistance; large coils with large wire and a small number of turns will have tens of ohms. If no resistance is measured at all, the inductance is open.

Other Failures

Inductors become defective because insulation breaks down and turns short together or the coil shorts to the core. Simple continuity checks with an ohmmeter between one end of the coil and the core detect the coil shorted to the core, but a few shorted turns on an inductor are very difficult to detect. If one-half the coil shorts out, resistance checks should detect it, but for a few turns, very accurate measurements must be made in order to detect that the coil is defective.

TRANSFORMER BASICS

As shown in *Figure 4-10*, a transformer is a device for coupling ac power from a source to a load. A conventional transformer consists of two or more windings on a core that are isolated from each other. Energy is coupled from one winding to another by a changing magnetic field. An ac voltage applied across the primary results in primary current. The changing current sets up an expanding and collapsing magnetic field which cuts the turns of the secondary winding. This changing magnetic field induces an ac voltage in the secondary which produces a current in any load connected across the secondary.

Figure 4-10. Simple Transformer

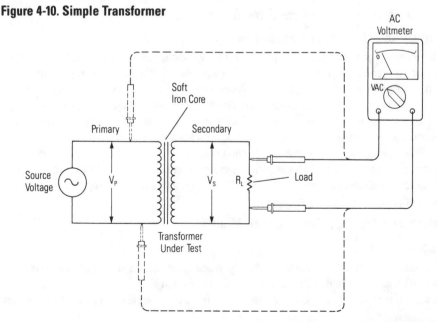

The core around which the primary and secondary are wound may be iron for low frequencies, as in the case of power and audio transformers. Primary and secondary windings on an air core may be employed for transformers that couple energy in higher frequency circuits.

Ideal Transformer

If the transformer were ideal, there would be no power loss from primary to secondary and 100% of the source power would be delivered to the load. Since voltage times current equals power, the power relationship is given by:

$$V_P \times I_P = V_S \times I_S$$

where V_P = primary voltage in volts
   I_P = primary current in amperes
   V_S = secondary voltage in volts
   I_S = secondary current in amperes

In an ideal transformer, the ratio of primary voltage V_P to V_S, the voltage induced in the secondary, is the same as the ratio of the number of turns in the primary N_P to the number of turns in the secondary N_S. The following equation expresses the relationship:

$$\frac{V_P}{V_S} = \frac{N_P}{N_S}$$

The turns ratio of a transformer is:

$$\frac{N_S}{N_P}$$

the ratio of the secondary turns to the primary turns.

Step-Up and Step-Down Transformers

If the number of turns in the primary and the secondary are equal, then the voltages appearing across the primary and secondary are equal. This type of transformer with a one-to-one turns ratio is called an isolation transformer. If a lower voltage appears across the secondary than across the primary, it is called a step-down transformer. The turns ratio would be less than 1. However, if a higher voltage appears across the secondary than across the primary, it is called a step-up transformer. The turns ratio would be greater than 1. According to the primary and secondary power relationship equation given previously, the secondary current will be stepped down if the secondary voltage is stepped up; and if the secondary voltage is stepped down, the secondary current is stepped up.

Resistance Testing of Transformer Windings

• Continuity

Resistance test with an ohmmeter may be made on most small transformers that are used in electronics to determine the continuity of each winding. Comparison of the measured resistance with the published data from the manufacturer should determine if a suspected transformer is defective. Power transformers and audio output transformers usually have their windings color coded so that the respective winding can be measured with an ohmmeter to determine if there is continuity, and to measure the winding resistance. If the winding measures infinite resistance, the winding is open. The break may occur at the beginning or end of the winding where the connections are made to the terminal leads. This type of break may possibly be repaired by resoldering the leads to the winding. If the discontinuity is deeper in the transformer, the transformer will have to be replaced.

If the winding resistance is very high compared to its rated value, there may be a cold solder joint at the terminal connections. If the condition cannot be corrected, the transformer will have to be replaced.

● Shorts — Primary and Secondary

A short from a winding to the core or to another winding may be found by measuring the resistance on a high ohms scale from core to the winding or from winding to winding. Place the ohmmeter leads on the winding lead and on the core, or across from one winding lead to another winding lead. Any continuity reading at all would indicate leakage to the winding from the core or between windings and indicate a defective transformer. A few shorted turns are difficult to detect but if a large percentage of the transformer is shorted out, resistance measurements will detect it.

The winding-to-core or winding-to-winding resistance of a transformer or an inductor can be tested with a voltmeter and a dc power supply as shown in *Figure 4-11*. The voltmeter will read zero if there is no breakdown between windings and core. If there is significant voltage read on the voltmeter, then there is a significant reduction in the interwinding resistance and the transformer is going bad.

Figure 4-11. Using a Voltage to Test an Inductor for Breakdown Between Winding and Core

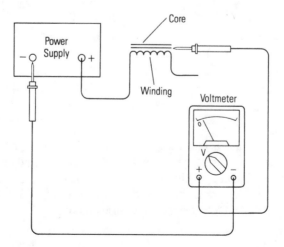

• Turns Ratio

The turns ratio of a transformer can be measured using the circuit of *Figure 4-10*. Apply a small ac voltage to the primary (V_P in *Figure 4-10*). A good source for this is a doorbell transformer. It supplies from 12 to 18 volts ac. Measure V_P with an ac voltmeter as shown in *Figure 4-10*. Now measure the secondary voltage V_s with the same voltmeter. The turns ratio,

$$\frac{N_S}{N_P}$$

is equal to

$$\frac{V_S}{V_P}$$

the secondary voltage divided by the primary voltage.

• Step-Up Transformer

Example: If V_P applied is 12 volts and V_S is measured as 60 volts, then the turns ratio is:

$$\frac{N_S}{N_P} = \frac{V_S}{V_P} = \frac{60V}{12V}$$

or

$$\frac{N_S}{N_P} = \frac{5}{1}$$

The turns ratio is 5:1.

• Step-Down Transformer

If the transformer is a known step-down transformer and the primary voltage is known, then the 110 VAC line voltage can be applied to the primary and the stepped down voltage read with the voltmeter.

Example: If V_P is 110 volts and V_S is 10 volts, then

$$\frac{N_S}{N_P} = \frac{V_S}{V_P} = \frac{10V}{110V}$$

or

$$\frac{N_S}{N_P} = \frac{1}{11}$$

The turns ratio is 1:11.

If the primary voltage is unknown, or whether it is a step-up or step-down transformer, it may be dangerous to place 110 volts across a winding because the secondary voltage could be quite high if it has a step-up turns ratio. Thus, applying a lower voltage for the turns ratio measurement is a much safer condition. In each case, the secondary is not loaded when measuring the voltage to determine the turns ratio.

MEASURING SEMICONDUCTOR DEVICES

The only definite test for a transistor is operating it in the circuit for which it was designed. However, there are several tests that can indicate the condition of its junctions. There are sophisticated tests that can be made with oscilloscopes, curve tracers, and switching characteristics checkers, but we want to show how it is possible to test a transistor or other semiconductor device fairly completely with only an ohmmeter.

Diodes

The diode is a two-terminal, non-linear device which presents a relatively low resistance to current in one direction and a relatively high resistance in the other. A "perfect" diode would act like a switch-either ON (Conducting) or OFF (Not Conducting) depending on the voltage polarities applied to the terminals. The typical construction and circuit symbol of a diode are shown in *Figure 4-12a* and *4-12b*. The cathode of a diode is usually identified by some means of marking. On small-signal glass or plastic diodes, a colored band or dot may be used (*Figure 4-12c*). For rectifiers, sometimes a + is used to indicate the cathode (*Figure 4-12e*), or metal can devices have a large flange on the cathode (*Figure 4-12d*).

Figure 4-13 shows a diode being tested with an ohmmeter. The proper indication is a high resistance reading when the ohmmeter plus (+) lead is on the cathode (N material) (Reverse Biased — *Figure 4-13b*), and a low resistance reading when the plus (+) lead is on the anode (P material) (Forward Biased — *Figure 4-13a*). A low resistance both directions indicates a shorted diode; a high resistance both directions indicates an open diode. A condition were, respectively, high current has destroyed internal connections, or high voltage has broken down the junctions.

Figure 4-12. Diode Construction, Symbol, and Identification

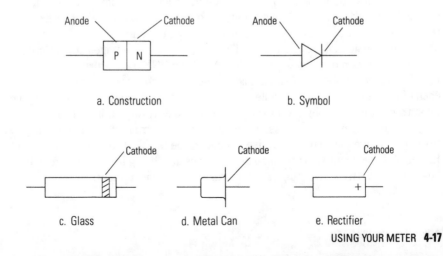

a. Construction   b. Symbol

c. Glass   d. Metal Can   e. Rectifier

Figure 4-13. Using an Ohmmeter to Measure a Diode

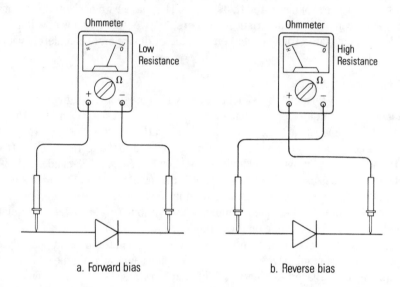

a. Forward bias   b. Reverse bias

Transistors

The transistor is a three-terminal device that has virtually replaced the vacuum tube. There are two basic types of transistors: the bipolar and the field-effect transistor.

Bipolar Junction Transistors (BJT)

A transistor is a device made of two PN junctions as shown in *Figure 4-14*. The transistor is basically an OFF device and must be turned ON by applying forward bias to the base-emitter junction.

Transistors can be considered as two diodes connected back-to-back. Therefore, each junction, like a diode, should show low forward resistance and high reverse resistance. These resistances can be measured with an ohmmeter and the results should be as indicated in *Figure 4-14*. The polarities of the voltages applied are shown to indicate forward or reverse bias on the NPN and PNP transistors.

The same ohmmeter range should be used for each pair of measurements to each of the elements (base-to-collector, base-to-emitter, emitter-to-collector). For most transistors, any ohmmeter range is acceptable. However, in some meters, the R × 1 range may provide excessive current for a small transistor. Also, the highest resistance range may have excessive voltage at the terminals of some ohmmeters. Either of these conditions may damage the transistor being tested. As a result it is best to start with the mid ranges for the resistance measurements.

Figure 4-14. Resistance Readings Across Junctions of Transistors

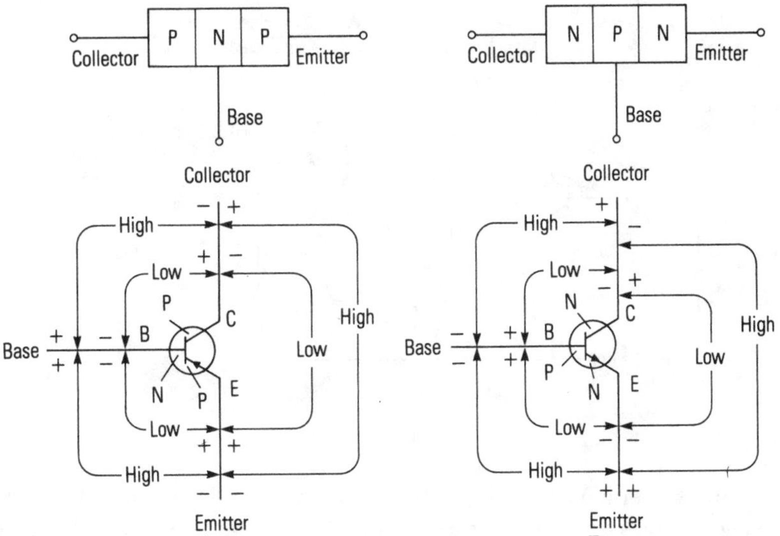

a. PNP   b. NPN

● Defects

If the reverse resistance reading is low but not shorted, the transistor is leaky. If both forward and reverse readings are very high, the transistor is open. If the forward and reverse readings are the same or nearly equal, the transistor is defective. A typical resistance in the forward direction is 100 to 500 ohms. However, a low power transistor might show only a few ohms resistance in the forward direction, especially at the base-emitter junction. Reverse resistances are typically 20K to several hundred thousand ohms. Typically a transistor will show a ratio of at least 100 or so between the reverse resistance and forward resistance. Of course, the greater the ratio the better the device is for an application.

Operational Test of a BJT

The amplification action of a transistor may be checked with the circuit of *Figure 4-15*. It will give some indication if the transistor is operational. Normally, there will be little or no current between the emitter and collector (I_{CEO}) until the base-emitter junction is forward-biased. Therefore, a basic operational test of a transistor can be made using an ohmmeter. The R × 1 range should be used. Closing S_1 will allow a small base bias current to be applied from the ohmmeter internal battery through R_1.

Figure 4-15. Operational Test of Transistor with Ohmmeter

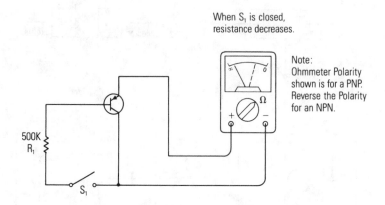

When S₁ is closed, resistance decreases.

Note:
Ohmmeter Polarity shown is for a PNP. Reverse the Polarity for an NPN.

If the transistor is operational, the base current will cause collector current to flow, thus reducing the collector to emitter resistance. The ohmmeter shows a decreased resistance (an increased emitter-collector current) when S_1 is closed to indicate that the transistor is operational and amplifier action is taking place.

Field-Effect Transistors

A field-effect transistor (FET) is a voltage operated device that requires virtually no input current. This gives them an extremely high input resistance. There are two major categories of field-effect transistors: junction FETs and insulated gate FETs, more commonly known as MOS (metal-oxide-semiconductor) field-effect transistors. Like the bipolar junction transistor, the FET is available in two polarities: P-channel and N-channel.

The schematic symbols for field-effect transistors are given in *Figure 4-16*. Notice the terminals are identical for N-channel and P-channel but the arrow on the gate terminal is reversed. This also indicates that the current direction from source-to-drain depends on the polarity type of the FET. Since there is no set designation for the source and drain terminals of the FET, the reference manual or the equipment schematic should be consulted to identify the terminals on the FET being tested.

Testing FETs is somewhat more complicated than a bipolar junction transistor. First, determine from all markings if the device is a JFET or an MOS type. Otherwise, the terminal measurements will have to indicate the type. Do not attempt to remove it from the circuit or handle a FET unless certain that it is a JFET or a MOSFET with protected inputs. If one touches the leads of these devices, static electricity can damage an unprotected device very quickly. Make certain all static electricity is grounded out before handling FETs.

Figure 4-16. Field-Effect Transistors

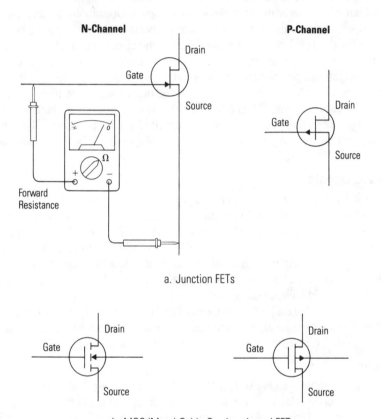

a. Junction FETs

b. MOS (Metal-Oxide-Semiconductor) FETs

J-FET Measurements

To test the forward resistance of the JFET gate to source junction, use a low voltage ohmmeter on the R × 100 scale (or nearest to it). For an N-channel JFET, connect the positive lead to the gate (see *Figure 4-16a*) and the negative lead to either the source or drain. Reverse the leads for a P-channel. The resistance should be less than 1K ohms.

To test the reverse resistance of the N-channel JFET junction, reverse the ohmmeter leads and connect the negative lead of the ohmmeter to the gate and the positive lead to the source or drain. The device should show almost infinite resistance. Lower readings indicate either leakage or a short. Reverse the leads for a P-channel JFET.

Operational Test of a JFET

The following simple out-of-circuit test will demonstrate if a junction FET is operational but will not indicate if the device is marginal. Operational means it is not shorted or open, which is by far the most common occurrence when a FET becomes defective. After the JFET has been removed from the circuit, connect the ohmmeter between the drain and source terminals. Touch the gate lead with a finger and observe the ohmmeter polarity connections to the source and drain terminals and the channel type (P or N). Reverse the leads of the ohmmeter to the terminals and again touch the gate terminal. The ohmmeter should indicate a small change in the resistance opposite to that previously observed if the FET is operational. The change in resistance will be very slight and some operational (good) FETs will not appear to change.

MOS Measurements

To test a MOSFET, the device must be handled with caution and the hands and instruments must be discharged to ground before measurements are made. If a MOSFET is to be checked for gate leakage or breakdown, a low voltage ohmmeter on its highest resistance scale should be used. The MOSFET has an extremely high input resistance and should measure "infinity" from the gate to any other terminal. Lower readings indicate a breakdown in the gate insulation. The measurements from source to drain should indicate some finite resistance. This is the distinguishing characteristic of a MOSFET; it has no forward and reverse junction resistance because the metal gate is insulated from the source and drain by silicon oxide. It should be a very high resistance with both polarities of voltage applied.

SCR Testing

An SCR is a gated diode that is used for the control of ac power. If a positive voltage is applied to the anode relative to the cathode, the diode will not conduct in the forward direction until triggered by current in the gate. Once triggered on, the diode is turned off by the voltage between anode and cathode going to zero. Testing with an ohmmeter is not recommended for high current SCRs and should only be used as a relative indication in low current SCRs. The current supplied by the ohmmeter may not be enough to "fire" or "hold" the SCR and therefore may not always indicate the true junction condition of the device.

However, a simple test of low power SCRs may provide an approximate evaluation of their gate-firing capabilities by connecting an ohmmeter as shown in *Figure 4-17*. The negative lead is connected to the cathode and the positive lead to the anode. Use the R $\times$ 1 scale on the ohmmeter. Short the gate to the anode with S_1. This should turn the SCR "ON" and a reading of 10-50 ohms is normal. When S_1 is opened and the gate-to-anode short is removed, the low resistance reading should remain until the ohmmeter lead is removed from the anode or the cathode. Now, reconnecting the ohmmeter leads to the anode and cathode should show a high resistance until S_1 is closed again to short the gate to the anode.

Figure 4-17. SCR Testing with Ohmmeter

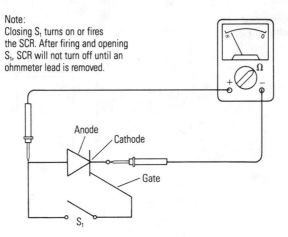

Note:
Closing S₁ turns on or fires
the SCR. After firing and opening
S₁, SCR will not turn off until an
ohmmeter lead is removed.

TESTING A BATTERY

A battery is a single cell or group of cells that generate electricity from an internal chemical reaction. Its purpose is to provide a source of steady dc voltage of fixed polarity. The battery, like every source, has an internal resistance that affects its output voltage. For a good cell, the internal resistance is very low with typical values less than an ohm. As the cell deteriorates, its internal resistance increases preventing the cell from producing its normal terminal voltage when there is load current. A dry cell loses its ability to produce an output voltage even when it is out of use and stored on a shelf. There are several reasons for this, but mainly it is because of self-discharge within the cell and loss of moisture in the electrolyte. Therefore, batteries should be used as soon after manufactured as possible. The shelf life is shorter for smaller cells and for used cells.

Testing Under Load

A very "weak" (high internal resistance) battery can have almost normal terminal voltage with an open circuit or no load current. Thus, a battery should be checked under its normal load condition; i.e., in the equipment that it powers with the power switch on. Out of the equipment, the only meaningful test is with a load resistor across the battery as in *Figure 4-18*. The value of the load resistor depends on the battery being tested. For a standard "D" cell, R_L = 10 ohms; a "C" cell, R_L = 20 ohms; an "AA" cell, R_L = 100 ohms; and a 9-volt battery, R_L = 330 ohms.

Figure 4-18. Testing a Battery Under Load

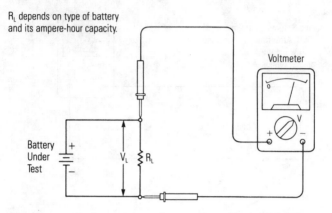

The terminal voltage should not drop to less than 80% of its rated value under load. The internal resistance may be calculated by the equation

$$R_I = \frac{V_{NL} - V_L}{I_L}$$

where V_{NL} = the terminal voltage, unloaded
  V_L = the terminal voltage with a load resistor
  I_L = the load current which is equal to:

$$\frac{V_L}{R_L}$$

Measure V_{NL} first without a load, then measure V_L with a load, and calculate the internal resistance.

● Current Drain

The current drain of a battery should be measured in its actual operating condition; that is, with its normal load. It can be measured by connecting the current meter in series between the battery and the equipment it is powering. The battery clip may be disconnected from the battery on one side and the current meter connected to complete the circuit. The correct polarity must be observed. Start on a high current range in case of an excessively high current due to a malfunction.

Now that we have found out how to make measurements on individual components, let's look at how to measure components in circuits. That is the subject of the next chapter.

MEASUREMENT OF CIRCUIT COMPONENTS

The most popular and versatile instrument on any electronics technician's workbench or in his toolbox is the multitester or multimeter. Understanding how to use multitesters to measure individual components is important, but understanding how to use them in making measurements in a circuit, the subject of this chapter, enhances their value many times over.

ABOUT IN-CIRCUIT COMPONENT TESTS

General Considerations

In-circuit measurements with a multitester usually occur with power applied to the circuit. These measurements usually are made because something has happened to cause a circuit, or a device, or a piece of equipment to operate improperly. Measurements are being made to locate the problem. This is called troubleshooting the circuit. Because power is applied special safety precautions should be observed. Make certain that measurement terminals are not shorted together or to ground by the test leads. This is especially so when 110 VAC line voltage is being measured. Severe shock or extensive damage can result if caution is not exercised.

Meter Safety

The multitester will remain a valuable servant if reasonable care is taken while operating it. Specification limits should not be exceeded. Start out with high ranges when the value of the measurement is unknown, then move to lower ranges to bring the meter deflection upscale.

CHECKING A DC POWER SUPPLY

Each electronic system has a power supply, even if it is simply a battery. Let's look at a typical simple dc power supply, and how its voltage can be measured.

Basic Circuit Understanding

Typically, electronic power supplies consist of rectifiers, diodes, transformers, a filter made of capacitors and inductors or resistors, and a bleeder resistor, which can be used also as a voltage divider. *Figure 5-1* shows a popular power supply circuit.

This circuit uses a full-wave, center-taped rectifier circuit to convert the ac voltage delivered by the transformer to dc. The pulsating current from the rectifier is smoothed by the filter. The bleeder resistors serve at least two purposes here. They provide multiple outputs, including one negative voltage with respect to ground. They also provide a constant minimum load for the power supply to draw a minimum current and stabilize the output voltage.

Normal Operation Reference Values

Normal values of dc voltage, ac voltage, and resistances to ground expected in the circuit are very valuable reference values to a technician troubleshooting a power supply. *Table 5-1* shows some typical values for the circuit of *Figure 5-1* that should prove very useful.

Figure 5-1. A Popular Power Supply Circuit

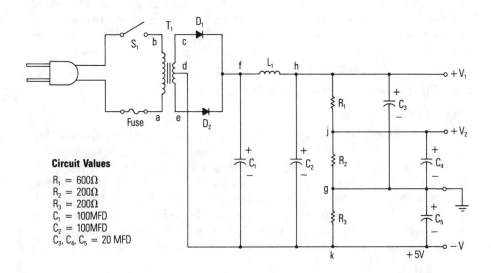

Circuit Values

$R_1 = 600\Omega$
$R_2 = 200\Omega$
$R_3 = 200\Omega$
$C_1 = 100MFD$
$C_2 = 100MFD$
$C_3, C_4, C_5 = 20\ MFD$

Table 5-1. Normal Voltage and Resistance Measurements

	VOLTAGE MEASUREMENTS		
Type	Test Points	No Load Voltage Value	R to g
ac	a-b	110VAC	∞
ac	c-e	40VAC	$R_3 \| R_1 + R_2$
ac	c-d	20VAC	$R_3 \| R_1 + R_2$
dc	f-g	+20V	$R_1 + R_2$
dc	h-g	+20V	$R_1 + R_2$
dc	j-g	+5V	R_2
dc	k-g	−5V	R_3

Locating Defective Components

Suppose in the circuit of *Figure 5-1*, that there is no voltage between point h and ground. In order to isolate the problem, a measurement is made to determine if input ac voltage is present. This ac voltage is measured between points c and e. If there is no voltage across c and e, it would indicate trouble due to defects in any of the following:

a. open line cord or defective line outlet plug.

b. open fuse.

c. open switch.

d. open transformer.

Voltage, continuity and resistance measurements are used to find and correct the problem.

If the above is not the problem and voltage is present at points c and e, then it is likely that the defect would be:

a. the load.

b. the rectifiers.

c. the filter inductor.

d. an open in the wiring between points c-e and h.

Disconnect the load from points V_1, V_2, and V_3. If the voltage at h returns, then the problem is in the load. If not, check b, c or d. Voltage and resistance measurements to ground with *Table 5-1* as a reference should isolate the problem.

Resistance Measurements

NOTE: Before measuring resistance, turn power OFF and discharge all capacitors, especially if they are electrolytic. Specific circuit test points are selected so that resistance measurements can be made from the test points to ground to determine if there are circuit shorts or circuit opens. For example, if one of the filter capacitors is shorted (say C_2), the resistance from point h to ground will be zero. When the trouble is found and the faulty component located and replaced, perform an operational check on the supply to make sure it is completely repaired.

TROUBLESHOOTING A SIMPLE AC CIRCUIT

A Doorbell Circuit — How It Works

Figure 5-2 shows a typical doorbell circuit. This circuit has the doorbell and switch in series with the transformer secondary winding. The doorbell operates at 10 VAC. This low voltage is not dangerous, and as long as the measurements are made on the secondary side of the transformer, it is not necessary to turn off the circuit breaker to check out the circuit. The voltage measurements for a normally working doorbell circuit of *Figure 5-2* are shown when the button is not pushed and when the button is pushed. M_1, M_2 and M_3 are different meter readings. If any of the voltages are not correct, the listed readings should help to determine the power supply problem. If not, then resistance measurements will have to be made. *[NOTE: Turn the circuit breaker off (or remove fuse) before making resistance measurements.]* The resistances for a normally working doorbell circuit also are shown in *Figure 5-2*.

Figure 5-2. A Typical Doorbell Circuit

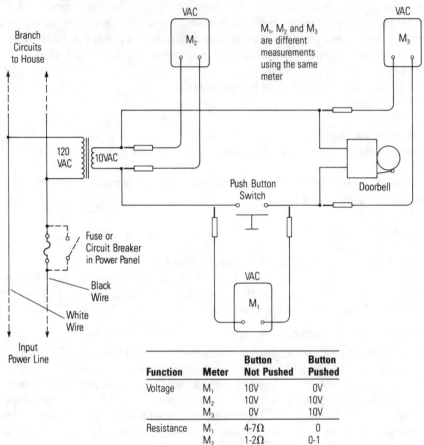

Function	Meter	Button Not Pushed	Button Pushed
Voltage	M_1	10V	0V
	M_2	10V	10V
	M_3	0V	10V
Resistance	M_1	4-7Ω	0
	M_2	1-2Ω	0-1
	M_3	2-5Ω	0-1

When The Bell Doesn't Ring

Assume that the bell does not operate when the button switch is pushed. The two most common problems are a bad switch or a bad bell. To track down the trouble, measure the voltage across the push button switch. With the switch open, 10 volts should appear across the open switch. There is no current in the circuit and thus no voltage across the bell (M_3). When the switch is closed, meter M_1 should read zero. If a voltage appears across the switch even when it is closed, this indicates that the circuit is not operating properly. Check the contacts to see if they are corroded or broken. The switch can possibly be repaired by simply scraping and cleaning the contacts. However, it may have to be replaced. If 10 volts appears across the bell when the button is pushed and the bell does not ring, the bell is probably defective. Disconnect it and check its resistance to see if it has an open coil.

Tracing a Short Circuit

Now let's assume that instead of an open we have a short in the circuit. We'll use voltage readings to find the short in the circuit. Assume that M_1 reads the normal zero volts when the switch button is pushed. However, M_1 reads an abnormal value of only 2-3 volts when the switch is open. It should read 10 volts. Now, measure the voltage across the transformer secondary (M_2). It also is a low reading of 2-3 volts. You note that the transformer is quite warm. You suspect a short so you disconnect one of the wires to the secondary, the M_2 voltage jumps to 10 volts. This indicates that there is a short circuit somewhere in the leads going to the doorbell. This short circuit drains so much current from the transformer secondary that it is overloaded and the output voltage is reduced to the low value of 2-3 volts.

To locate the trouble, examine the wires for frayed or worn insulation and possible points where they may touch. Sometimes a nail is driven through the wires scoring the insulation and causing the wires to short out with age. When you find the short, clear it and check for normal voltages as indicated above.

TROUBLESHOOTING YOUR TELEPHONE INSTALLATION

The fact that we can pick up our telephone and talk to almost anyone in the world is surely a modern miracle. Its dependability is amazing; however, there can be problems. Though you are not allowed to do repair work on the equipment owned by the local telephone company, you can make simple tests on the line and your own telephone instruments.

Testing the Telephone Line

A good way to determine if the trouble is on the telephone line or in one of the instruments is by substitution. If you plug a telephone that is known to be good into the line and it does not work, then you have verified that the line has the problem. If everything works, you know that the first instrument is the problem. If the trouble is on the line from the telephone company's central office to where it enters the house, the telephone company repairman will have to do the repairs. However, if the trouble is in your house, you can repair it yourself.

On Hook and Off Hook

The most common place for a telephone line to connect initially as it comes in from the outside is a 42A terminal block. *Figure 5-3a* shows a 42A terminal block and *Figure 5-3b* shows how four phone jacks are wired from the block. The incoming line and the branch lines can be tested with a VOM or a DVM. The dc voltage between the red and green wires should be about 48 volts with all of the telephones either "on hook" (hung up) or unplugged from their jacks. The minus ($-$) lead of the meter is connected to the red (ring) terminal and the plus ($+$) meter lead is connected to the green (tip) terminal. An open or a short on the line can result in a zero voltage reading at a jack.

Figure 5-3. Initial Connection of Incoming Telephone Line

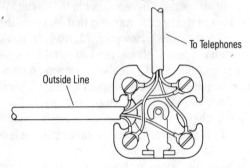

a. 42A Block

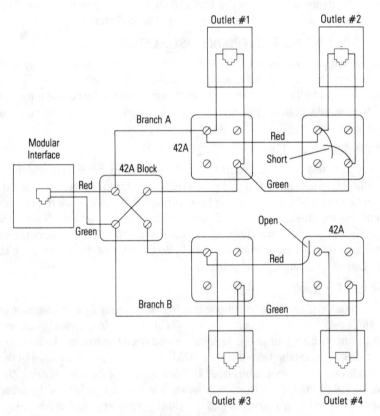

b. Interconnection

The voltage that will be measured across the line in the "off hook" condition (hand piece lifted and ready for use) will depend on several things; mainly the distance from the central office and the wire size used for the phone line. Typically the voltage will be from 5 to 10 volts dc.

Testing Branch Circuits

Let us now consider how to find a short or open at some point on one of the lines shown in *Figure 5-3b*. First, we will determine that the trouble is in the home and not on the phone line from the central office. At the 42A terminal block where the outside line enters the house, remove all the branch lines and measure the voltage. There should be about 48 volts dc with the red lead negative (−) and the green lead positive (+). Let us assume this is as it should be. A telephone set can be connected here and the line further confirmed to be good.

There are two branches from the 42A block: Branch A with two outlets, #1, and #2; and Branch B with two outlets; #3, and #4. None of the outlets will work with a telephone set.

When Branch A is reconnected to the 42A, the 48 volts goes to zero. This means a short somewhere on Branch A. Going to outlet #1 and visually inspecting the connections indicates no short. If the wires that feed outlet #2 are removed at outlet #1 (even just one of them), the voltage at outlet #1 now measures 48 volts. A telephone instrument may be plugged in and it will work fine. Reconnecting the feed line to outlet #2 again kills outlet #1. Examination of the wiring at outlet #2 shows that the two wires are shorted together. After the short is cleared, outlets #1 and #2 work fine.

Branch B is now reconnected and outlet #3 checks okay but #4 does not. It has no voltage. Examination of the wiring of outlet #4 turns up a broken red wire, and therefore, an open circuit. Reconnecting the red wire to the outlet terminal screw restores voltage and operation to outlets #3, and #4. Plugging in a good telephone in all outlets shows that the system is operating properly.

Testing the Telephone Set

If it was determined that a telephone set is not operating properly, three problems are very common. A switch contact is bad, the talk and listen circuits are faulty, or the ringing circuit does not operate. Three quick tests can be made to isolate these problems.

● Measuring Resistance

In order to determine if the switchhook contacts are operating properly, the resistance of the telephone set can be checked with an ohmmeter. Measure between the red and green wires leading to the telephone set with the set disconnected from its outlets or from the 42A block. This measurement is shown in *Figure 5-4*. With the handset on hook, the resistance should be infinity; with the handset off hook, the resistance should be 2000 to 10,000 ohms. Any reading below 1000 ohms indicates some problem with the telephone set. Further detailed troubleshooting would be necessary to locate the problem.

By measuring with an ohmmeter as shown in *Figure 5-4*, a clicking will be heard from the receiver of the handset to indicate that the talk and listen circuits are working properly. If the transmitter is an electrodynamic microphone, the clicks also will be heard from the mouthpiece.

Figure 5-4. Measuring the Handset with an Ohmmeter

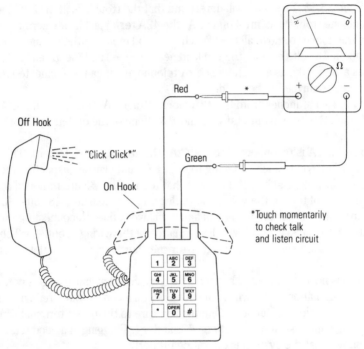

• Test of the Ringer Circuit

The easiest way to test the telephone set for ringer problems is to measure if ringing voltage is available. With the telephone set connected to the line, the handset on hook, and a voltmeter connected across the line as shown in *Figure 5-5* at the 42A block (or the initial entry point into the house or apartment), have a friend or relative call your number. Ninety (90) volts ac voltage is applied at the central office across the line when the telephone is to ring. The amount of voltage at the telephone set depends on the distance from the central office. If the voltage appears but the telephone does not ring, more detailed troubleshooting would have to be done to locate the specific problem with the ringer. Be careful not to touch the wires with your hands or fingers. The ac ringing voltage can shock you.

OPERATION OF A BJT CIRCUIT

Normal Operation

Figure 5-6 is a typical kind of circuit that uses a BJT (bipolar junction transistor), in this case an NPN transistor, to be the active device in an amplifier circuit. Certain conditions must be met to make the transistor circuit operate properly. The base and emitter junction must be forward biased in order for the transistor to be turned on and conduct current. If the base and emitter junction is reverse biased (lack of forward bias) the transistor will be turned off and will not conduct current.

Figure 5-5. Measuring Ringing Voltage

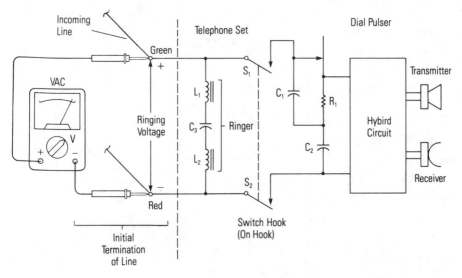

The letters NPN or PNP tell us much of what we need to know about the voltages in the circuit for normal operation. For example, the center letter (P in NPN) means the base must be positive with respect to the emitter to forward-bias it. P must be positive and N negative to forward bias a PN junction. This letter also tells the polarity of the power supply applied to the collector in a BJT amplifier circuit, since the collector-to-base junction must be reverse biased. If the transistor is an NPN, a positive voltage is applied to the collector compared to the base and vice versa for a PNP. As the base voltage of an NPN transistor is increased with respect to the emitter, the base current increases, which increases the collector current. As the base-to-emitter voltage is decreased, the less the transistor conducts, until it stops completely. A conducting transistor normally has a high resistance between collector and emitter until it is driven into the saturation region (the region where the collector is only a few tenths of a volt away from the base). In a saturated transistor the resistance is low, and an increase in base bias (forward) results in no further increase in collector current. A saturated transistor may be considered near a dead short. Conversely, a cutoff transistor (one that has no collector current except leakage current) is a very high resistance, near an open circuit.

Measuring Voltages

An easy way to evaluate whether a transistor is operating properly in a circuit such as *Figure 5-6* is to measure the voltages at the collector, base and emitter while the transistor is in the circuit. *Figure 5-6* gives typical voltage values when measuring the voltage from ground to the respective transistor element of an NPN BJT.

Figure 5-6. Transistor Amplifier for Normal Operation

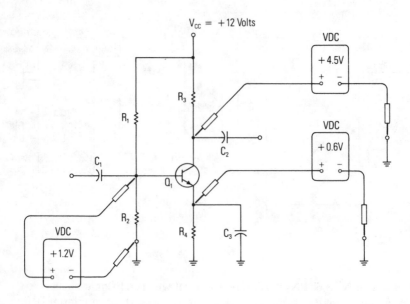

The voltages could have been measured between the transistor electrodes, that is, from element to element, but the most common way, and the way most voltage values are given in service manuals and on schematics, is to have ground as a common reference as shown in *Figure 5-6*. Ground is usually the chassis into which the circuit is mounted, and very normally one terminal of the power supply.

● *Junction Voltages*

Silicon transistors normally have a difference of 0.6 to 0.8 volts between the emitter and base with the polarities depending on the type of transistor (NPN or PNP). As mentioned previously, the voltage between emitter and base will be in the direction to forward bias the junction; that is, positive on P material and negative on N material. The collector-base junction is reverse biased, positive on the N and negative on the P. If the transistor amplifier happened to be made with a germanium transistor, the emitter-to-base voltage would be 0.2 to 0.3 volts. The types and polarities are the same as silicon.

● Steady-State No Signal Voltages

Voltages given in *Figure 5-6* are the steady-state no-signal bias voltages. The transistor amplifier will usually be operated Class A, which means that the signal will increase or decrease the current in the transistor from that due to the no-signal bias voltages. Little change will occur in the emitter-to-base voltages, but large changes can occur in the collector-to-base (or collector-to-ground) voltage due to the voltage drop in the load resistor, R_3, caused by the signal current change. The amount of shift is an indication of the amplifer's gain.

Parallel Resistance Check

One of the simplest test to determine that the transistor is operating properly in the circuit is to place a resistor R_X equal in value to R_1 across R_1 (in parallel) in the circuit. As shown in *Figure 5-7,* if the voltages are measured at the base, emitter and collector with respect to ground, we see that the voltages at the base and emitter are increased over what they were in *Figure 5-6,* indicating an increased base current. The collector voltage is decreased due to the increased voltage drop across R_3 due to the increased collector current resulting from the increased base current. The emitter current and voltage has increased due to the increased base current and increased collector current.

Figure 5-7. Increasing Transistor Current by Paralleling R₁

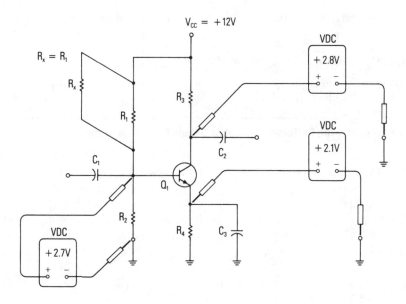

Measuring Current Gain

Transistors basically are current amplifying devices. The small-signal current gain is the gain that is active in producing the amplification in Class A small-signal amplifiers like that shown in *Figure 5-6*. Even though the small-signal current gain and the dc current gain are not directly correlated, the dc current gain can be used as an indicator of the relative small-signal current gain available from a transistor. To measure the dc current gain, the base current and collector current can be measured as shown in *Figure 5-8*, and the dc current gain, h_{FE}, commonly called "Beta," can be calculated.

The common problem with *Figure 5-8* is that circuit leads must be broken to insert the current meters. To avoid breaking the circuit, voltage measurements can be made across resistors as shown in *Figure 5-9*, and by using Ohm's law, the current through the resistors can be calculated. For example,

$$I_1 = \frac{V_1}{R_1}$$

$$I_2 = \frac{V_2}{R_2}$$

$$I_3 = \frac{V_3}{R_3}$$

$$I_4 = \frac{V_4}{R_4}$$

The collector current is I_3, the emitter current is I_4, and the base current, I_B, is

$$I_B = I_1 - I_2$$

Therefore, h_{FE} or Beta can be calculated using

$$h_{FE} = \frac{I_C}{I_B} = \frac{I_3}{I_1 - I_2}$$

Figure 5-8. Measuring Collector Current and Base Current to Calculate Current Gain

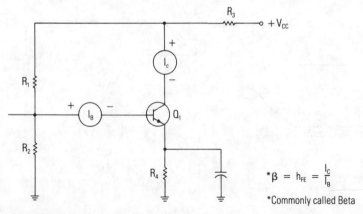

$$*\beta = h_{FE} = \frac{I_C}{I_B}$$

*Commonly called Beta

Figure 5-9. Using Voltage Measurements to Calculate Currents

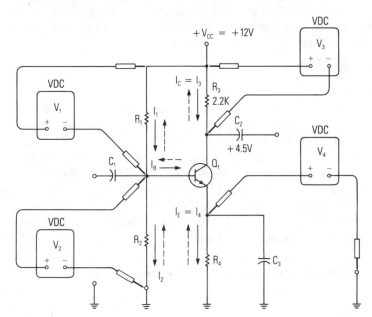

DEFECTIVE TRANSISTORS

Open Junctions

If the transistor becomes defective, the most common faults are for a transistor junction to either breakdown because of overvoltage and short out, or to burn out because of excessive current and open. If a junction opens, the transistor will no longer draw current. The most obvious measurement to detect this condition is a measurement of the collector voltage. If the collector does not draw current, the collector voltage will be very near to the supply voltage. This voltage will be considerably higher than the voltage shown in *Figure 5-6* as the normal no-signal steady-state operating voltage. There may not be a great deal of difference in the base voltage if the base-emitter junction opens because its voltage is commonly set by the bias resistor network of R_1 and R_2, and not changed much if the small current into the base is stopped.

Shorted Junctions

If a junction is shorted, more than normal current is likely to flow and operating voltages will be affected accordingly. Suppose the collector-to-base junction is shorted. Now the collector voltage is likely to be much lower than normal because the current is controlled by the short circuit and not by the transistor. In addition, the base voltage is likely to be much different because of the loss of isolation of the collector junction.

If the emitter-to-base junction is shorted, the transistor action will stop. As a result, the collector voltage should be very close to supply voltage, emitter voltage will be the same as base voltage and the transistor is disabled. This case is shown in *Figure 5-10*, where a physical short has been placed across base and emitter with a clip lead. The voltage measurements are shown.

DEFECTIVE RESISTORS

Open R₁

Even though it is quite rare, let's demonstrate how BJT circuits can be analyzed considering the effect of certain resistor failures; that is, particular resistors opening or shorting. What would happen if R_1 of *Figure 5-6* were to open? The voltage that result are shown in *Figure 5-11*. The no-signal steady-state condition of the transistor is not forward-biased and the collector is at the supply voltage. If a resistor doesn't have current through it, there will not be a voltage drop across it. The output signal, if any, would be grossly distorted. It would only be negatively going. Any negative-going portion of the input signal would be clipped off because any signal present would be capacitively coupled to the base.

Figure 5-10. Shorting Base-to-Emitter to Turn the Transistor Off

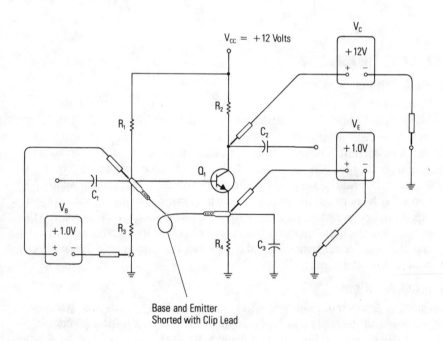

Base and Emitter
Shorted with Clip Lead

Figure 5-11. Voltages Resulting from an Open R₁

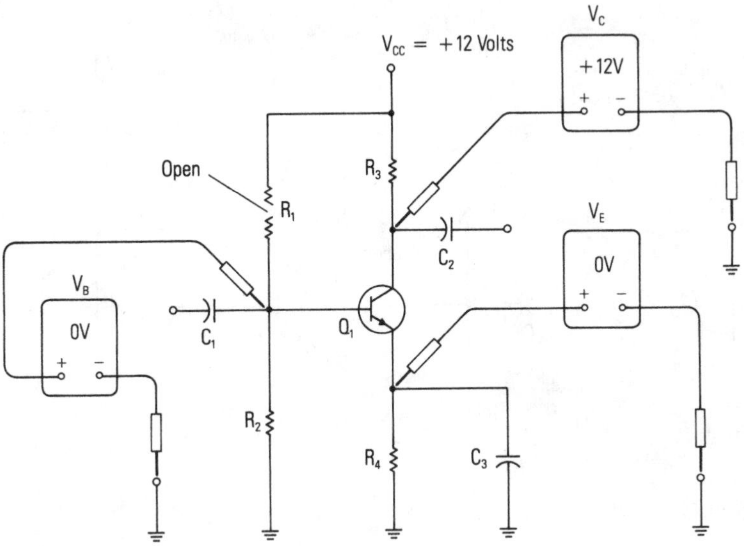

Shorted R₁

What would happen if R_1 were shorted? A short across R_1 puts a very high forward-bias voltage on the base. The resistance of R_3 and R_4 in series is the only limit to collector current. The base-emitter current is limited only by R_4. It is likely that the transistor will be destroyed. The initial voltages are shown in *Figure 5-12*. Note that the collector and emitter voltages are the same. The transistor is said to be in saturation.

Open and Shorted R₂

An open R_2 produces an increase in current similar to that discussed above for R_1 shorted. Since the current through R_2 is now zero, there is less current through R_1. The voltage drop across R_1 is much less and the base voltage is much greater. The base current, in fact, rises to a value that completely turns on, or saturates, the transistor. Its collector voltage will be only about 0.1 volt above the emitter voltage and it cannot amplify signals. A short across R_2 is very similar to the condition shown in *Figure 5-10* except the base and emitter voltages are zero.

Open R₃

Now consider R_3. If this load resistor is open as shown in *Figure 5-13*, the collector current is zero. Any emitter current must now be supplied by the base. The base-emitter junction acts like a forward-biased diode which places R_4 in parallel with R_2. Since R_4 is a small value of resistance, the emitter voltage falls to a very low value. As can be expected, the base voltage will be its normal 0.6-0.7 volts above the emitter voltage.

Figure 5-12. Voltages Resulting from a Short Across R₁, Q₁ is in Saturation

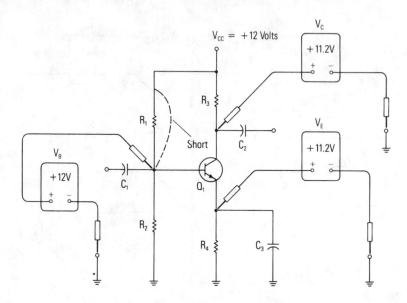

Figure 5-13. Voltage Resulting from Open Load Resistor R₃

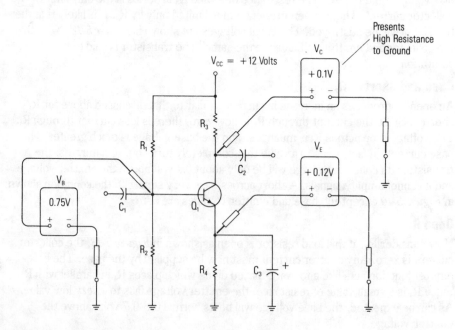

It might be assumed that the collector voltage would read zero since the load resistor is open. However, when a voltmeter is connected, it presents a high resistance path from the collector to ground. The collector-base junction acts like a forward-biased diode allowing a small current through the meter. Note the voltage from base-to-collector is $0.75 - 0.1 = 0.65$ volts in the forward-bias direction.

Open R$_4$

Figure 5-14 shows the voltage values that result when R$_4$ opens. Since all transistor current is through the emitter lead, with an open circuit between the emitter and ground there is no current through the transistor. The collector voltage rises to V$_{cc}$ because of no voltage drop across R$_3$. The voltage at the base is a result of the voltage divider R$_1$ and R$_2$, and because the base current is relatively insignificant, it remains almost unchanged. The voltage at the emitter depends on the resistance of the voltmeter used to measure it. When it is connected, a small emitter current exists because the meter's resistance replaces R$_4$. Therefore, the voltage at the emitter is slightly higher than normal. If the voltmeter measuring emitter voltage is left in place and the collector voltage measured, the collector voltage will be lower than +12 volts because some small collector current will flow due to the completed emitter circuit.

Figure 5-14. Voltages Resulting from an Open Emitter Resistor R$_4$

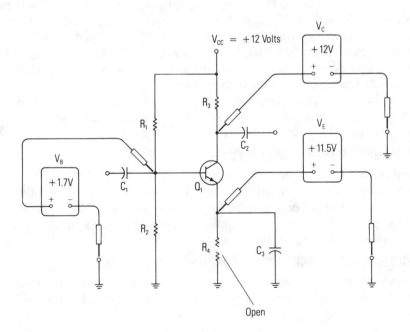

Shorted R$_4$

A shorted R$_4$ is equivalent to a shorted C$_3$ since they are in parallel. Because capacitor shorts are common (resistor shorts are rare) this condition is more likely to occur than any we have discussed. The emitter voltage reads zero. The transistor, heavily forward-biased, saturates and passes a current limited by V$_{cc}$ divided by R$_3$. This normally prevents the transistor from being damaged. The base voltage will be clamped 0.7 volts above the emitter and the collector will measure 0.1 volts above the base. This is the approximate saturation voltage of a silicon transistor.

The function of C$_3$ is to provide an ac signal bypass across or around the bias stabilization resistor R$_4$. If C$_3$ is open, an ac signal voltage will appear across R$_4$ introducing negative feedback into the amplifier circuit. The gain of the stage will be reduced by a value close to the ratio of R$_3$/R$_4$. The dc voltages will remain unchanged. A quick check is to shunt (parallel) the bypass capacitor C$_3$ with a known good capacitor of the same value. *CAUTION:* Shut off the power before connecting the shunt capacitor to prevent a large surge current from damaging Q$_1$. Then reapply power.

A FIELD-EFFECT TRANSISTOR AMPLIFIER

An operating FET amplifier is shown in *Figure 5-15*. The normal operating no-signal steady-state voltages are shown. Although the functions of the capacitors in the FET amplifier circuit are similar to those in the BJT amplifier circuit, the results of failure are not necessarily the same. The values of capacitance are much smaller due to the higher impedances in the FET circuit. In the case where C$_1$ shorts in the FET circuit of *Figure 5-15*, the voltage from the preceeding stage will be coupled to the gate and will increase the current through the FET. In some cases C$_1$ will only be leaky and not be shorted. Any voltmeter reading above zero at the gate indicates a leaky C$_1$. With a leaky C$_1$, only a small portion of the voltage coupled from the previous stage will appear on the gate, but the effect is the same. A leaky C$_1$ reduces the reverse bias on the gate causing the drain current to increase, which will cause the drain voltage to be lower than the steady-state value and restrict the signal swing.

TYPICAL AMPLIFIER IN RADIO OR TV

Figure 5-16 shows a transistor amplifier circuit that might be designed into a television or radio receiver. Note that although the power supply voltages within the system are quite a bit higher than in the previous circuits, resistor divider circuits are used to step down the supply voltage for the circuit to the normal static voltages used in the previous circuits. R$_8$ may or may not be present.

GROUND REFERENCE AND CIRCUIT CONFIGURATION

Sometimes circuits are drawn or wired so that they look different from *Figure 5-6*. However, as far as the transistor is concerned, the operating conditions are the same.

Figure 5-15. A Typical FET Amplifier Circuit

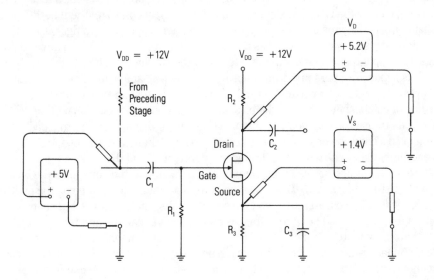

Figure 5-16. A Typical Amplifier in a TV or Radio Set

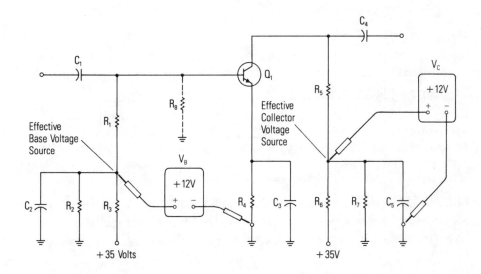

Look at *Figure 5-17* and compare it to *Figure 5-6*. Though the positive power supply terminal is at ground, the base bias network and collector load resistors are returned to ground also. The emitter resistor R_4 and the bottom base bias resistor R_2 are connected to the negative supply terminal. It is important to realize that the transistor bias voltages between its elements are identical in the two figures and that is what matters. If ground is used as a reference, the voltages will be negative. If the negative supply terminal is used as a reference, the voltages will be positive.

It is a matter of personal preference of some technicians to measure the voltage between elements of transistors directly. This is the fastest and least confusing method of establishing whether the bias on a transistor is correct. The method of specifying transistor voltages on schematics and in service manuals is from each element to a common or ground. The technician must then take the voltage measurement at each element to ground and subtract to find the bias voltage (difference in voltage between the elements). For example, the voltage on the base of the transistor in *Figure 5-17* is -8.0 volts from ground. The voltage on the emitter is -8.6 volts. The base-emitter voltage is $+0.6$ volts, the difference between -8.0 volts and -8.6 volts. The base voltage is more positive than the emitter voltage.

With this chapter we have completed the individual component measurements and the measurement of components in circuits. In the next chapter we will look at common types of measurements that normally are made around the home.

Figure 5-17. Transistor Amplifier Stage with Positive Ground Power Supply

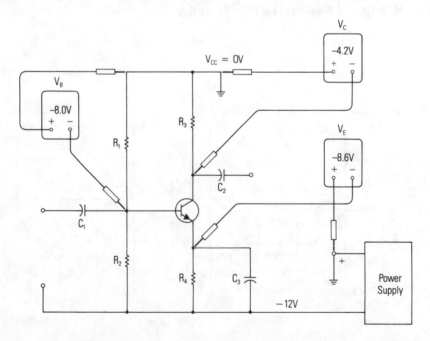

MEASUREMENTS AROUND THE HOME

OBJECTIVE

Having dealt with the measurement of components individually and in circuits, we now wish to summarize the various uses of a meter by discussing common measurements that one can make around the home to verify proper electrical circuit operation, identify a circuit problem if there is one, and correct or repair any improper operation. We will go through several applications in detail to indicate the procedure. Other applications will not include as much detail, but with schematics and our explanation of the circuit performance, the reader should be able to use similar procedures to check the circuit performance.

POWER DISTRIBUTION AND ELECTRIC LIGHTING

Even though Benjamin Franklin did his kite experiment with electricity in the 1700s and drew many important conclusions still practiced today, it wasn't until Thomas Edison invented the common light bulb (called an incandescent lamp) in 1879 that common use of electricity became widespread. Let's look at how electrical power is distributed.

Lighting Circuit

Figure 6-1 shows a common home power distribution panel. Three circuits are shown. A lighting circuit which has light bulbs wired across (in parallel) a 110-120VAC leg of the incoming power distribution. A 15 ampere circuit breaker is in series with one side of the line. The light bulb sockets are connected to the lighting circuit by quick connectors, called wire nuts, the plastic protectors that screw over wires twisted together. To measure the voltage at a light socket, an ac voltmeter on the 150V range or greater is used to measure the voltage at the twisted wire connections after the plastic wire nuts are removed. Or one lead of the voltmeter can be placed on the light switch terminal as shown. If the current is to be measured, and a clip-on ammeter is not available, the circuit can be broken at the circuit breaker and an ammeter inserted. EXTREME CAUTION: *Make sure the main power switch is turned off before making this connection. In fact, as shown in Figure 6-1, make sure there is no voltage at Point A before inserting an ammeter.* With two 100W bulbs on the circuit, it would read approximately two amperes.

Figure 6-1. Home Power Distribution

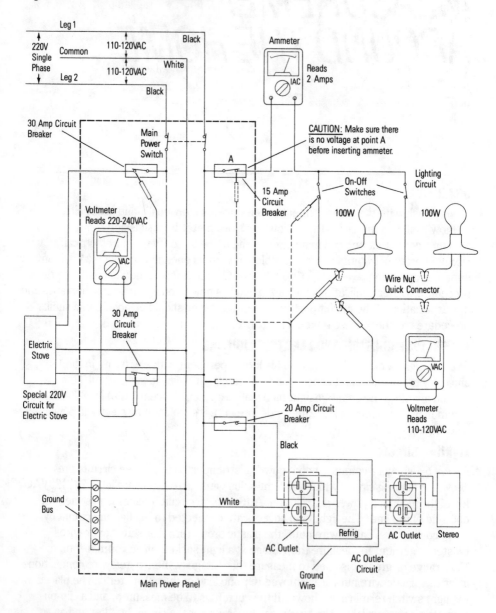

Outlet Circuit

An ac outlet circuit is shown with a refrigerator and a stereo plugged into outlets. If it is suspected that an ac outlet is not functioning properly, the ac voltage at the receptacle can be measured as shown in *Figure 6-2* by following these steps:

1. Remove the suspected outlet receptacle face plate by removing the center screw.
2. Plug a lamp into a receptacle on the same circuit. Turn on the lamp.
3. At the power distribution panel, throw the circuit breaker OFF to turn off the lamp. This turns power off to the circuit feeding the receptacle; therefore, there is no danger of electrical shock as the receptacle is removed.
4. Remove the screws that hold the suspected outlet receptacle in the box.
5. Pull out the receptacle as shown in *Figure 6-2*.
6. Throw the circuit breaker ON back at the panel.
7. Measure the voltage at the receptacle as shown in *Figure 6-2*.
8. If there is no voltage look for broken wires, loose screws, or a damaged or cracked outlet.
9. Continue to isolate the problem by elimination working back to the power panel. Some outlets receive their power by wires inserted into spring contacts at the receptacle. These spring contacts, in many cases, become defective and make poor contact. The connection is broken if the spring contacts do not make good connection.

Figure 6-2. Measuring 110-120 VAC at Receptacle

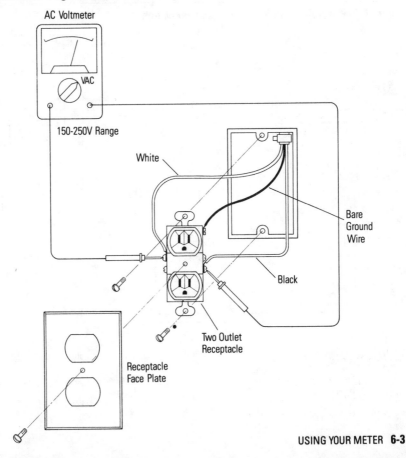

● *220VAC Circuit*

In addition, a special 220VAC circuit is shown for an electric stove. It is connected across both incoming power legs. As shown, the voltage can be measured easily by placing a meter across the two circuit breakers that are in separate voltage legs in the power panel. As a result, the 220V measurement is much safer because no wires or wire nuts need be removed to make the measurement.

Power Loss

Whenever current passes through a resistance, power is consumed in the form of heat. This power loss is often called I^2R loss and sometimes occurs at places such as poor wire connections, loose fuse connections, and rough or dirty contact surfaces on switches. If a poor connection is suspected in such places, an IR drop test can be made with a voltmeter. Touch the voltmeter probes on each side of the suspected connection while it is under load. If there is unwanted resistance, a voltage drop will be read on the voltmeter. Then, with the power off, the ohmmeter can be used to measure the resistance in ohms. *Figure 6-3* illustrates this phenomenon and technique.

Figure 6-3. Possible High-Resistance Connections

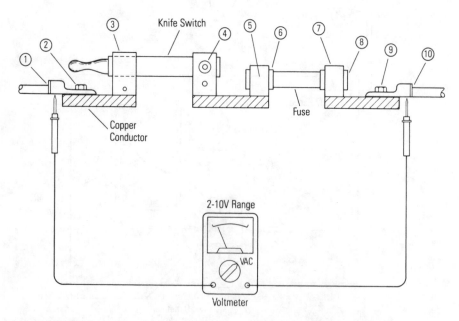

1. Pressure Connection to Conductor (Crimp)
2. Cap Screw
3. Switch Blade
4. Rivet Joint
5. Fuse Clip
6. Ferrule End Compression Connection
7. Fuse Clip
8. Ferrule End Compression Connection
9. Cap Screw
10. Pressure Connection to Conductor (Crimp)

Shorts and Ground Faults

A short circuit occurs when current takes an accidental path short of its intended circuit. It is caused by the creation of a path of significantly lower resistance than that of the normal circuit. A short circuit can be damaging to an electrical system because of excessive currents that occur under a short circuit condition. Short circuits are usually caused by insulation between parts breaking down or wires shorting together because of vibration.

A ground fault is an accidental connection of a non-grounded conductor with the equipment frame or case. It is a form of a short circuit that results in current leaving the circuit conductors and going through a path of other conducting materials provided by the frame. It is usually a fault in insulation.

Both short circuits and ground faults can be located with an ohmmeter. Check the circuit schematics of the equipment under test to determine the normal resistance in the circuit. CAUTION: *Be Sure That Power Is Off Before Measuring Ohms!*

Incandescent Lights

The incandescent lamp is basically a simple device whereby the electricity passing through the filament wire heats it so hot that it glows and gives off light. The amount of heat produced by the filament is determined by the wattage of the bulb. The wattage, in turn, is determined by the resistance and resultant current, according to Ohm's law, when a given voltage is applied. It is important to note that the resistance of the filament when it is cold is greater than it is when hot, so that a simple measurement with an ohmmeter will not be correct for finding the wattage of a lamp. The "hot" resistance can be found by measuring the voltage and the current, then dividing the voltage by the current to obtain the resistance.

The incandescent lamp is very versatile and is found in many applications such as a small flashlight bulb, Christmas tree lights, all of the lights in an automobile, outdoor and street lights, and many other applications. Even though the incandescent lamp is most common, other types of lamps are often used for various purposes. The fluorescent lamp is one of these.

● *Dual-Filament Bulbs*

A popular incandescent table or floor lamp today is one that has a dual-filament (three-way) bulb which permits a single lamp to be turned to dim, medium, and bright settings by a special switch that connects the filaments singly or in parallel as shown in *Figure 6-4*. If a floor or table lamp is defective, the voltage from line to switch is measured with an ac voltmeter, as shown in *Figure 6-4c, 6-4d,* and *6-4e*. If you want a quick check on a light bulb, the easiest measurement to make is a continuity measurement to make sure the filament(s) are not burned out. *Figure 6-4a* shows how to make a continuity check on the 3-way bulb using an ohmmeter. Continuity should be indicated, as shown in the schematic of *Figure 6-4b*, between the common outside base and the center contact A or the ring contact B. If the bulb where just a common single filament bulb, then there would only be a center contact A and the common base contact.

Figure 6-4. 3-Way Incandescent Lamp

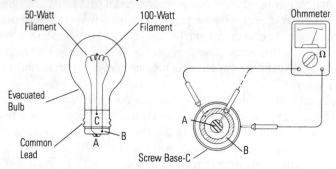

a. Inside View and Checking Continuity of a 3-Way Light Bulb

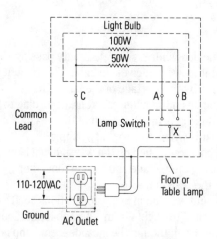

b. Schematic Diagram (Light Off)

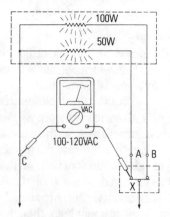

c. Dim Setting (50 Watts)

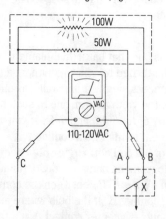

d. Medium Setting (100 Watts)

e. Bright Setting (150 Watts)

Fluorescent Lights

The fluorescent lamp was introduced in 1939 and is much more efficient than the incandescent lamp. Fluorescent lamps require a starter circuit to heat filaments before sufficient electrons are emitted to ionize the mercury vapor gas inside the tube. After the gas is ionized, the resistance of the lamp drops so low that if it were connected directly to the power line, it would draw so much current that it would burn out very quickly. Because of this fact, a current limiting device (a ballast) must be connected between the lamp and the power source. The fluorescent lamp circuit is shown in *Figure 6-5* with typical voltage measurements. If the starter never opens it would not allow the fluorescent bulb to light. The ballast and starter usually are contained within the fluorescent lamp's fixture. Some early fixtures had removeable starters.

Figure 6-5. Fluorescent Lamp

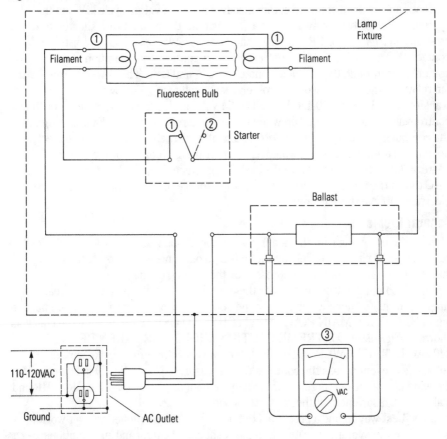

① Starter closed to allow filaments to heat to give off electrons to ionize mercury vapor.

② After mercury vapor is ionized starter opens.

③ Voltage across ballast low until vapor ionizes then high.

HEATING AND AIR CONDITIONING

One of the most common systems around the home is a heating and/or air conditioning system. In many homes, the furnace system to provide the heat is separate from a system to provide cooling. However, more and more homes are being built with a central system that contains both heating and air conditioning. We will use such a system as our example system. The heating system is a natural gas or electric hot-air distribution system and the air conditioning system is a freon system with compressor and condenser outside and the evaporator inside above the hot-air furnace. The furnace blower is used in both cases to distribute the hot or cold air throughout the house.

Electrical Circuit

Figure 6-6 shows a typical schematic wiring diagram for the example central heating and air conditioning system. The thermostat has two switches. One that controls the system function — HEAT, COOL or OFF, and one that controls the fan either to be on continuously or to come on automatically when the system cycles. When the system switch or the fan switch is in a set position, the contacts are shorted together as shown in *Figure 6-6*. FR is a relay that controls a two-speed fan motor through contacts FR_1 and FR_2. CR is a control relay that controls the operation of the compressor through the dual-line contactors CR_1 and CR_2. The power source for the fan relay and the compressor control relay is 24 volts stepped down through a transformer TR_1 from 110-120 VAC. The 24 volts is also the power source for the gas control valve which is turned on when heat is required. A gas pilot ignites the gas in the combustion chamber. In *Figure 6-6,* a heater relay also is shown for an electric heating system. The system would have either the gas control or the electric heaters. Once the fan relay is energized, the contacts FR_1 and FR_2 connect 110-120 VAC to run the motor. 220 VAC is the power source for the compressor and the electric heater, if there is one.

General Problems

Most of the problems with the heating or air conditioning system will be in the low voltage control circuits. Rarely do the relays go out, unless their contacts are burned due to a short in the motor, compressor or the heating element.

If the compressor doesn't run or the electric heating element doesn't heat, a simple continuity check will indicate if the compressor or heating element are burned out. THROW ALL MAIN POWER SWITCHES TO OFF before making the check as shown in *Figure 6-6*. EXTREME CAUTION SHOULD BE TAKEN BECAUSE 220VAC IS THE POWER SOURCE. Check with a voltmeter to make sure no voltage is present across the contacts to be measured. No continuity indicates that the windings of the compressor or heating element are open. Find the CR or HR and make the measurement at the contacts as shown in *Figure 6-6*.

The best way to find a problem if the heater or air conditioner doesn't work is to isolate the system operation into the respective heating and air conditioning functions.

Figure 6-6. Typical Central Heating and Air Conditioning System

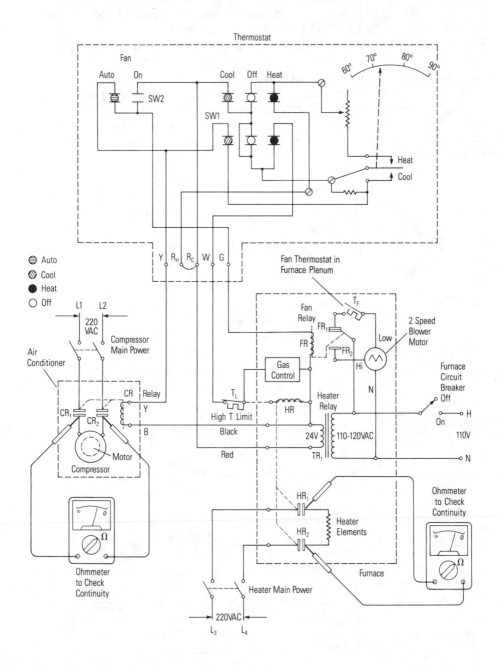

Heat Cycles

Figure 6-7 shows the schematic of *Figure 6-6* when in the heating mode. Only the circuitry associated with the heating function is shown. The function switch is in the HEAT position and the fan switch is in the AUTO position. If the system is operating properly, the thermostat contacts TH_H would be closed because the thermostat was turned up to a temperature higher than the temperature of the space to be heated; thus, demanding heat. Closing TH_H energizes the gas control (or the heater relay) turning on the gas flow which burns and generates heat. As soon as the inside of the furnace heat exchanger reaches the T_F temperature, the thermal switch T_F closes and energizes the low speed of the fan motor through the closed contacts FR_1. When

Figure 6-7. Heat Cycle

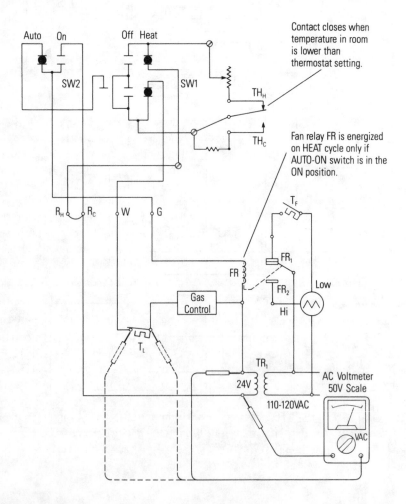

the room temperature rises and causes TH_H to open, the fan motor continues to run until the furnace plenum is cool enough to cause T_F to open. If the AUTO-ON switch is placed in the ON position, FR is energized, the high speed of the fan motor is energized through contacts FR_2, and the circuit through contacts FR_1 is opened. Heated air is delivered to the space to be heated. If the temperature inside the furnace ever exceeded T_L, the thermal switch T_L would open and disconnect the power from the gas control to shut off the gas. Of course, for a gas furnace, the pilot light must be on before the gas control will work, so *if the furnace is not heating the pilot may have gone out,* or the pilot gas control thermocouple may be defective and must be replaced.

If the pilot is on and the furnace does not come on when the thermostat is turned up, follow these steps:

1. Remove the panel from the furnace and the cover from the thermostat.
2. Measure the voltage across the secondary of the 24V low voltage control transformer as shown in *Figure 6-7.* If there is no voltage at the secondary, measure the 110-120 VAC at the primary. If there is no primary voltage, check the furnace circuit breaker at the power panel. If there is primary voltage and no secondary voltage, turn off power and measure the continuity of the secondary to make sure it is not burned out.
3. If 24V is present, manually operate TH so that TH_H closes and determine if gas flows and the furnace flame comes on. If gas does not come on, switch SW_1 from OFF to HEAT several times to determine if the switch contacts may be corroded and not completing the circuit correctly. Voltage measurements around the loop as shown in *Figure 6-7* should isolate the problem.
4. The same procedure can be used to isolate a problem in the fan circuit. However, a first easy check of the fan circuit is to turn the fan switch to ON, which will make the relay operate and the fan to run continuously. If this is not the case, operate the switch several times, maybe the contacts are corroded. A common problem is that the thermal switch, T_F, has gone bad. Make voltage measurements around the circuit to isolate the problem. The 24 volts will be safe and will not shock you, but be very careful when making measurements in the 110VAC fan motor circuit.

Cool Cycles

Figure 6-8 is the schematic when the system switches are set to COOL and the fan switch is on automatic. The temperature in the space to be cooled is higher than the thermostat setting, thus TH_C is closed to demand cooling. When TH_C closes, it completes the circuit to supply 24 volts to CR the compressor control relay. The compressor runs and supplies coolant to the evaporator mounted in the air flow path in the furnace.

At the same time the TH_C completes the circuit for CR, it also completes the circuit to supply power to the fan relay FR through the fan switch in the AUTO position. This turns on the blower motor and the room air is driven over the evaporator to supply cool air to the space to be cooled.

Isolating a Problem

Obviously, if the air conditioning system is not cooling, many problems could be present besides the electrical circuit; therefore, a qualified air conditioning repair person must be called to isolate the problem. However, several simple checks will determine that the electrical circuit is operating properly.

● Fan Or Blower Motor Circuit

First of all, the fan circuit can be checked easily by placing the fan switch in the ON position. This should make the furnace blower run continuously. As shown in *Figure 6-8,* moving the fan switch to ON completes the circuit to supply 24 volts directly from the secondary of TR$_1$ to FR, the fan relay. If the fan does not come on, move the fan switch from AUTO to ON several times; the contacts may be corroded and the movement may burnish them to make contact.

Figure 6-8. Cool Cycle

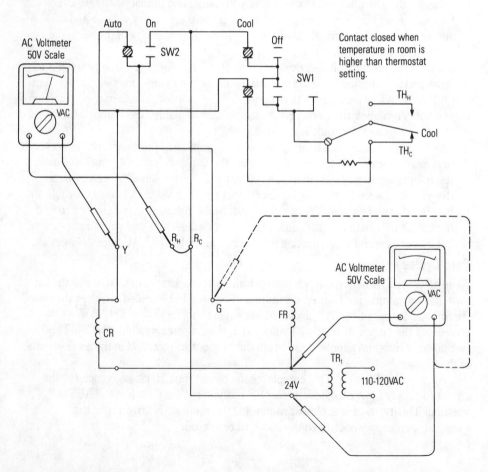

If the fan still does not come on, remove the furnace panel and isolate FR and TR_1. First measure the secondary of TR_1 to assure that the transformer is operating properly and supplying 24 volts, second, measure voltages around the circuit as shown in *Figure 6-8* to isolate the problem. The FR relay will make a noise when it operates. If it operates when the fan switch is turned to ON but the blower doesn't come on, then there may be problems with the contacts FR_2 of *Figure 6-6* and *Figure 6-7*, or the blower motor may be burned out. *WITH THE FURNACE AND AIR CONDITIONER CIRCUIT BREAKERS OFF AT THE POWER PANEL* continuity checks can isolate the problem.

• Compressor Circuit

The compressor control relay CR receives its 24 volts supply through a circuit that is completed through the contacts of SW_1 when the switch is in the COOL position. CR will be located in the air conditioning condenser that is mounted outside the house or building to be cooled. The compressor controlled by CR is also located there. If the temperature in the room is higher than the thermostat setting, TH_C should be closed and CR should operate when SW_1 is placed in the COOL position. A person located near the condenser can hear CR operate when SW_1 is placed in the COOL position. The compressor should turn on when CR operates. If CR is operating and the compressor turns on, and the blower motor turns on, but the unit still does not cool, an air conditioning specialist should be called.

If CR does not operate, then check to determine that TR_1 is supplying 24 volts properly. An easy check of this is to remove the thermostat cover and measure the voltage at Y and R_C, R_H of *Figure 6-8*. When TH_C is open (thermostat set higher than temperature in the room) then the voltage across R_C, R_H and Y should be 24 VAC. When TH_C is closed, the voltage should be zero volts. Just with these simple checks one can determine if the electrical circuits are operating properly.

If CR operates but the compressor does not come on, the contacts CR_1 and CR_2 may be bad or the compressor may be burned out. Call an air conditioning specialist if the problem is isolated to this point. CAUTION: IF CR IS OPERATING PROPERLY AND THE COMPRESSOR COMES ON, DO NOT CYCLE THE COMPRESSOR FROM ON TO OFF RAPIDLY. IT MAY OVERHEAT THE COMPRESSOR AND CAUSE A THERMAL SWITCH INSIDE TO OPEN.

WASHER AND DRYER CIRCUITS

We will not go into detail with respect to locating and isolating problems with the washer and dryer electrical circuits. We will just present the circuit and a short description of the circuit operation and expect that, after the above examples and the material in the preceding chapters, the reader will be able to follow measurement procedures for continuity, voltage, current and resistance and isolate any problems. To that end the following are some overall guidelines.

Troubleshooting an Electrical System

In almost all cases, troubleshooting the electrical section of a system is straight forward and usually simple. Always apply basic rules of electrical theory when testing any circuit. Remember, if theory and practice do not agree, it means either incorrect theory or incorrect practice!

The first step in troubleshooting any circuit is to have a clear understanding of the circuit and its function before starting. If you do not understand how a circuit functions when there is no problem, it is almost impossible to troubleshoot the circuit because you may not know what you are looking for. This does not mean you must have a total understanding of the circuit, but it does mean that you must have a general overall knowledge of the circuit's function.

The next step is to eliminate the obvious, no matter how simple it may seem. This includes first checking the fuses, circuit breakers, and overload resets. If careful observation does not yield recognition of an out-of-the-ordinary condition, then the problem must be isolated to the control circuit, power circuit, load, or incoming power. Each of these areas, although connected and related, can be isolated one from the other to make troubleshooting easier.

The following is a step-by-step procedure.

1. Eliminate the incoming power supply as the source of problems by measuring the 220 volts or 110 volts that are the main supply. One of the most common troubles found in all electrical circuits is a blown fuse or tripped circuit breaker.

2. Usually the control circuit of most systems is at a low voltage — 24 volts is common. Isolate it and measure it and make sure it is operating properly. Usually the presence of the 24 volts can be used to indicate continuity through a particular branch of the control circuit.

3. Electric drive motors, fan motors, and heaters are common electrical loads. Electric motors are essentially reliable machines and require little maintenance in comparison to the rest of the circuit. Check the voltage at the motor to see if it is the correct level, that is, if it matches the nameplate voltage within 10%. If the voltage is correct at the motor, but it does not run, there may be an internal thermal switch in the motor that has become defective or is open because the motor is hot.

The electrical loads are controlled through relay contactors that are controlled by the low voltage circuit. Even though low voltage is present and the relay is operating, it does not mean that the contacts themselves are not defective.

WASHING MACHINE ELECTRICAL SYSTEM

The Electrical Circuit

One of the biggest stumbling blocks encountered when servicing an appliance is the variety of wiring diagrams or worse yet, the lack of a diagram at all. Each manufacturer has his own idea of a wiring diagram. Once you have interpreted the schematic, wiring diagram, and/or the operation chart, the appliance will be much easier to troubleshoot. *Figure 6-9* shows a typical wiring diagram as it would appear on the back of a washer. You will have to know what is suppose to happen and when it is suppose to happen before you can tell if there is anything wrong.

Timers

The timer in an appliance may be thought of as the "brain" of the machine, because it controls the sequence of operation. It generally consists of three basic components assembled into one unit:

1. The timer motor
2. The escapement
3. The cam switchbox.

Figure 6-9. Wiring Diagram of Automatic Washer Showing Electrical Connections from Timer to Other Electrical Parts

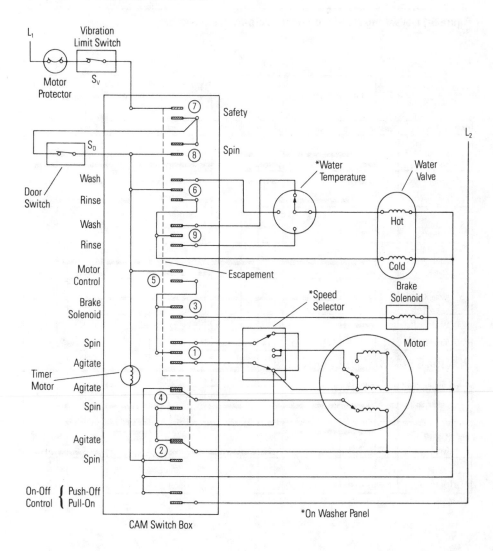

The motor is an electric-clock type geared down to a small pinion gear that drives the escapement, which drives cams in the cam switchbox to close switches 1 through 9 in a timed sequence. Obviously, if the timer motor is defective, only the motor should be replaced, not the entire timer. The purpose of the escapement is to rotate the cam shaft in a series of timed pulses. It is not generally serviceable and a problem here normally requires replacement of the total unit. The cams in a timer open and close the electrical switch contacts, thereby controlling the sequence of operations.

A cycle-sequence chart, shown in *Figure 6-10* tells when a circuit is active, and also at what time in a cycle a particular function is in progress.

Figure 6-10. Washing Machine Timer Cycle-Sequence Chart

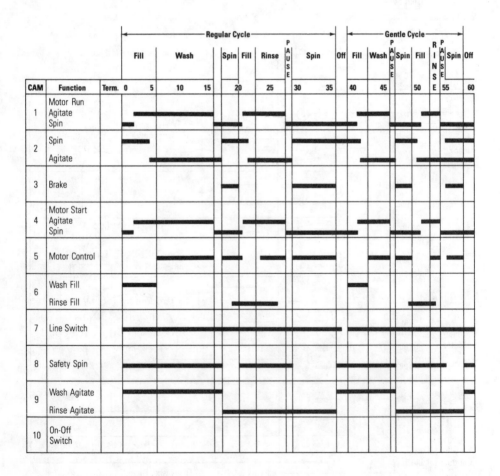

Safety Switches

There are switches that are designed to provide safer operation of the machine; For example, a switch to open and stop the spin action when the door is opened (S_D), or another to detect an unbalanced load (S_V). These switches are common suspects for open circuits. The water temperature and speed switches are not as likely to become defective.

Troubleshooting

With the aid of *Figure 6-9* and *6-10,* one can tell if voltage is to be applied to the motor or the hot or cold water valves. With power off, trace the circuit, using an ohmmeter for continuity, to locate accessible terminals where voltages can be measured. 110VAC can be measured to verify proper operation. No low voltage control voltage is available in this circuit. Be very careful not to short out the 110VAC.

DRYERS

The electrical circuit of dryers is very similar to washers in that it contains a timer motor, escapement and a cam switchbox. However, the circuit is much simpler because basically there is only one function being performed — blowing hot air through the clothes for a given amount of time to dry them. The heating element is resistance wire which glows when a voltage is applied. The voltage is 220-240VAC. The drive motor to turn the tub that tumbles the clothes operates from 110-120VAC. This motor also drives a blower that moves air through the dryer and vents it outside the dryer. The circuit diagram is shown in *Figure 6-11*. To understand the operation, let's look first at the safety switches.

Safety Features

If the drive motor is not turning the tub, there will be no power to the heating elements. The 220-240VAC circuit is held open by C_{F2}, the centrifugal switch that is on the drum drive and blower motor. C_{F2}, as well as C_{F1}, closes when the motor is at the correct speed. C_{F1} disconnects the start winding of the motor after the motor is at the correct speed. It also closes the circuit to the buzzer and the cool-down thermostat.

The cool-down thermostat closes when the temperature inside the dryer rises to its operating temperature. It does not open again until the temperature cools below this temperature. An exhaust temperature thermostat is located in the exhaust port of the dryer. It is normally closed and will not open unless the exhaust temperature exceeds a given temperature set by the manufacturer of the thermostat. As a double precaution against the dryer rising above a maximum temperature, there is a second safety switch in the heating element power circuit. It is a high-temperature safety thermostat that opens the circuit if the temperature were to rise above a maximum set by the thermostat.

No power will be applied to the drive motor or the control relay circuits unless the door of the dryer is closed. The door switch closes contacts D_1 and D_2 to complete the power circuits. No power could be applied to the heating elements because the control relay would have no power and contacts C_5 and C_6 would be open.

Figure 6-11. Wiring Diagram of a Typical Dryer

(Courtesy of Whirlpool Corporation)

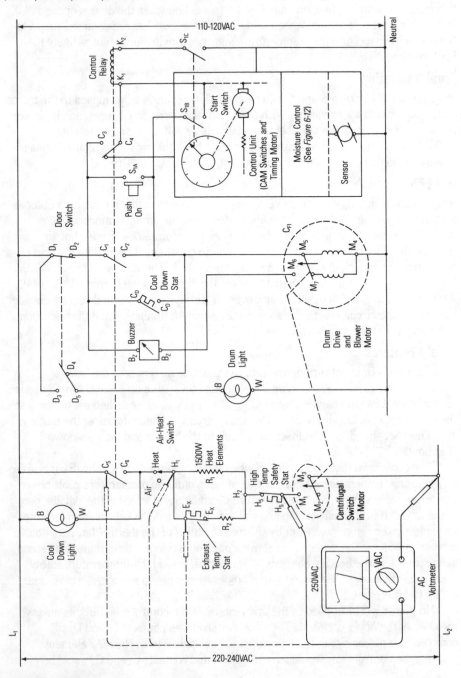

Dryer Operation

The start switch, S_{1B} and S_{1C} are closed by setting the timing control on the control unit to the appropriate time or time cycle desired. The power circuit to the control relay is completed by pressing the momentary push button, S_{1A}, which energizes the control relay and closes contacts C_1 and C_2, C_3 and C_4, and C_5 and C_6. C_1 and C_2 complete the power circuit to the drive motor for the drum and blower, and C_3 and C_4 complete a holding circuit for the control relay so it will remain energized after S_{1A} is released. C_5 and C_6 complete the power circuit to the heating elements if the air-heat switch is in the HEAT position. No power would be applied to the heating elements if the air-heat switch is in the AIR position. Just room temperature would be circulated through the clothes when in the AIR position.

When the timer times out, S_{1B} and S_{1C} are opened and the control relay is deenergized opening contacts C_1 and C_2, C_3 and C_4, and C_5 and C_6. Even though contacts C_1 and C_2 are open, the drive motor doesn't stop. The cool-down thermostat continues to complete the circuit until the temperature cools below the limit. The power circuit in this case is through the cool-down thermostat contacts C_D and through the M_6 and M_5 contacts of the centrifugal switch in the motor.

Once the cool down thermostat opens power is disconnected from the motor. However, until the motor slows down the M_6 and M_5 contacts remain closed to supply power momentarily to the buzzer that signals that drying is complete. Cool down is indicated by a light bulb that receives its power when C_5 and C_6 contacts of the control relay open. It remains on until the M_1 and M_3 centrifugal switch contacts in the heating element circuit open when the drive motor stops.

The circuitry is straightforward with door safety switches, temperatures sensitive switches that turn off the heating element if the temperature of the air over the clothes is too hot, and a centrifugal switch in series with the heating element that keeps the power circuit to the heating element open if the motor is not turning the tub. In other words, the motor that tumbles the clothes must be running before power is applied to the heater.

Troubleshooting a Dryer

A common problem with dryers is that the heating element burns out. With power off (pull the plug from the receptacle in the wall), check the continuity of the heating element with an ohmmeter. This can be done easily by removing the back panel. Check the schematic carefully to determine the proper interconnections.

If safety switches or thermostatic switches appear to be defective, voltage measurements should isolate any defective components. In *Figure 6-11,* an ac voltmeter on the 250VAC range is used to measure at various points in the heater element circuit. *This is a 220VAC circuit so measurements must be made very carefully.* Remember that the meter completes a circuit so that voltages will appear across open switch contacts if the rest of the circuit is complete. In many cases, if a switch is operating properly and the rest of the circuit is complete, 110VAC or 220VAC will appear across the contacts if the switch is open, and zero volts if the switch is closed.

Moisture Sensor Control

A different kind of control found on dryers is a moisture sensor to control the drying cycle. *Figure 6-12* shows such a circuit. T_M is the dryer timing motor that drives the cams and controls the switches in sequence. 110-120VAC supplies power to the circuit through L_1 and neutral.

The circuit works as follows. When wet or damp clothes are in the dryer and it is set on the cycle controlled by the sensor, S_D, the moisture across S_D will make it a low resistance. On the negative alteration of the ac line voltage, the diode D_1 conducts and drains current through R_5, R_4, and R_1. The voltage drop across R_4 (usually greater than 70 to 75 volts) causes the neon lamp N_1 to fire and draw current through R_3, R_2 and the SCR (Silicon Controlled Rectifier). The level of current is high enough to trigger the SCR. The triggered SCR effectively shorts out the timing motor and the timing motor stops.

When the clothes dry to the point where the sensor is no longer a low resistance, the current through R_4 no longer maintains a voltage drop high enough to fire the neon bulb. As a result, the triggering current to the SCR stops, the SCR turns off, and the timing motor starts and completes the drying cycle.

Troubleshooting the Sensor Circuit

The four components most likely to become defective are the sensor, the diode, the neon bulb and the SCR. If the dryer cycle is quite short so that the clothes never dry, anyone of these components could be at fault. One easy check for the neon bulb is to see if it glows when damp clothes are in the dryer. If it does, it is likely that the sensor, diode and neon bulb are all ok. The SCR may be defective.

If the neon bulb is glowing and the timing motor is running, it is a pretty fair indication that the SCR is defective. Remove it from the circuit and using an ohmmeter test the semiconductor junctions as discussed in Chapter 4.

If the neon bulb does not glow and the timing motor is running, measure the voltages at point 1, 2, 3 and 4. The voltage drop across S_D, R_5, D_1 and R_4 can be calculated as follows:

Voltage Drop Across
S_D	Voltage at Point 1
R_5	Point 2 − Point 1
D_1	Point 3 − Point 2
R_4	Point 4 − Point 3

If R_4 is a very small voltage, either the sensor S_D or the diode D_1 may be defective. Remove them from the circuit and measure S_D and D_1 independently as discussed in Chapter 3.

If D_1 is suspected as being defective, its forward and reverse resistance can be measured with an ohmmeter as shown in *Figure 6-12* if the power is removed from the dryer by removing the ac plug.

Figure 6-12. Electronic Dryness Control
(Courtesy of Whirlpool Corporation)

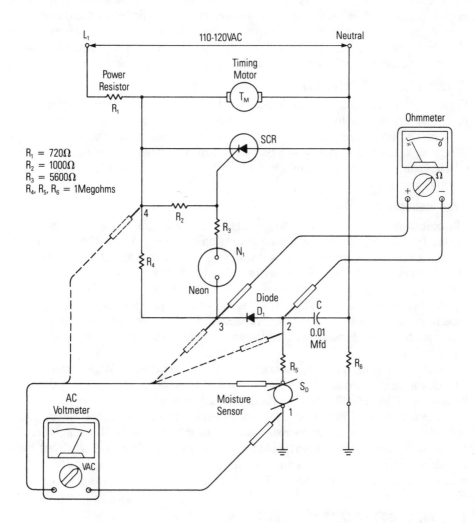

A SMOKE ALARM
The Circuit

There are two common types of smoke alarms in use: the ionization-chamber type, which is comparatively new, but widely distributed; and the photocell type, which has been widely used in industrial security systems for many decades, but has just recently been adapted to home use.

Ionization Chamber Detectors

In this system a tiny amount of radioactive material is mounted in a sensing chamber; it ionizes the air present, making it conductive. A 9-volt battery causes a flow of electric charges across the air gap of the sensing chamber. If fire-caused ions in the form of gases or smoke enter this ion chamber they interfere with the movement of electric charges across the air gap, causing a change in current. This is sensed by the electronic circuitry, which turns on the alarm, basically, an audio oscillator.

Photoelectric Cell Detectors

Basically the same principle as an infrared LED light source directed in a narrow beam that strikes a photocell and sets up a current is used here. However, a small baffle in the path prevents light directly from the LED from reaching the photocell. When smoke is present, it reflects a portion of light around the baffle to the photocell, which, in turn, triggers the alarm. On the outside, the two detectors look exactly alike.

Troubleshooting

The cost of most smoke alarms is so low that it is probably impractical to have them serviced. However, you can make some checks on it with your VOM. The system can be viewed as in *Figure 6-13*. Almost without exception, the detector, the battery, and the transducer are very similar in all smoke alarms. The two circuits on the PC board, however, will vary greatly. They may be contained in a single chip IC or be constructed of descrete components. If it is constructed with descrete resistors, capacitors, and transistors, trace the circuit using a VOM as an ohmmeter for a continuity tester. Then you can check the components in the circuit by the methods discussed in Chapter 2.

   The most obvious problem is a drained battery. The battery voltage, usually 9 volts, can be checked at the point where the leads enter the PC board, or at the battery clip (*Figure 6-13*). The transducer is usually one of two types of a ceramic piezoelectric buzzer. Either it is one with a built in driver, or else it is one requiring an external driver. The resistance across the transducer leads is about 16 ohms. Most smoke alarms have a test button that bypasses the transducer with a short circuit and sounds the alarm. This becomes an easy check on the battery. If the alarm does not sound under this check, measure the battery voltage with your VOM as shown in *Figure 6-13*.

TAPE OR CASSETTE RECORDERS/PLAYERS

The first tape recorders made use of open-reels for holding the tape. These have been replaced almost totally by the smaller, easier to use cassette version. Regardless of the type, a tape recorder/player also may have a built-in microphone, level meter, or a complete AM-FM radio.

Figure 6-13. A Basic Block Diagram of a Typical Smoke Alarm

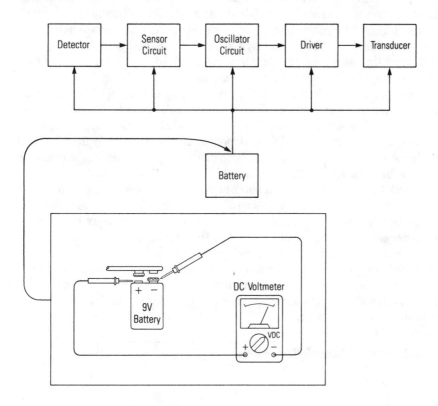

The Drive Motor

Drive systems, including the motor and the motor speed control, must produce steady and accurate drive power because the accurate reproduction of the recorded signal depends on a constant rate of tape motion across the head. Special control circuits such as PLL (phase locked loops) are used on the more expensive tape recorder systems to maintain constant speed. If it appears that the speed is varying, the voltage across the motor can be monitored with the DVM or VOM during the record/playback function to make sure there is no variation. If there is variation, check the transformer feeding the power supply or any capacitors in the power supply. If the drive is inoperative (the tape doesn't move) voltage measurements across the motor would be a first check. Absence of voltage would indicate trouble in the power supply; presence of proper voltage and no tape movement indicates a possible defective motor if one makes sure that the tape or any motor parts are not jammed. Turn off power and use an ohmmeter to check the motor's continuity and resistance.

Record/Playback Heads

Every tape system has at least one head and possibly two or three. Tape heads are basically electromagnets for converting audio amplifier signals into magnetic fields during recording, or for converting a magnetic field variation on the tape into an electric signal during playback. The magnetic tape moving across the heads acts as an abrasive that wears away the soft head metal. Head wear is the most common problem with tape heads but they can, because of the extremely small wire that is inside the head, open or short circuit. If there is no playback signal when in the PLAY mode, even from tapes that are known to have signals, a quick check should be made of the amplifier. The amplifier quick check can be made by plugging in a headphone and putting the recorder in the RECORD mode. Sounds picked up by the microphone should be heard in the headphone. If the amplifier is working properly, the trouble in a nonfunctioning recorder is in the head or the RECORD/PLAY switch.

To check the heads with an ohmmeter the connecting wires should be removed after carefully identifying them by making a brief sketch as shown in *Figure 6-14a*. With the leads disconnected, the resistance can be measured as shown in *Figure 6-14b*. Continuity should be obtained across the pins for each head. Make sure that the wires are reconnected exactly as they were removed.

If there is a signal from the tape when a known tape is played, but there is no playback signal when a recording has been made (in RECORD mode), then the record head should be checked in the same way as for the playback malfunction. If the head checks ok, check the RECORD/PLAY switch.

Figure 6-14. Checking Record/Playback Head

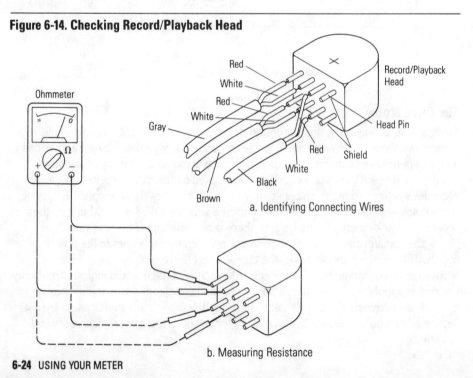

a. Identifying Connecting Wires

b. Measuring Resistance

The Amplifier
● POWER OUTPUT

The most common measurements of an audio amplifier are *power output* and *frequency response*. These tests can be made with a VOM since they involve basic voltage, current, and resistance measurements. Both power output and frequency response of an amplifier can be measured by the circuit interconnections shown in *Figure 6-15*. The input signal to the record amplifier is provided by the output of an audio oscillator connected through a plug into the microphone jack. As an alternate, an audio test tape may be used for the source of the test signal. The value of R connected across the shielded cable from the external speaker jack (or there may be an auxiliary output connection (or jack) on the back of the unit) should be equal to the rated output impedance of the amplifier (usually 4 or 8 ohms). The output power of the amplifier is proportional to the RMS voltage measured across the load resistor, in accordance with the power equation:

$$P = \frac{V^2_{output}}{R}$$

The audio oscillator should provide a good sine waveform output of uniform amplitude. Also, the amplifier must not distort the sine wave if the measurement is to be accurate. An approximate indication of whether the output signal is being "clipped" or distorted may be determined by observing the meter of the output. As the input signal is smoothly increased, the output voltage (and consequently power) will increase at the same smooth rate until clipping occurs. A reduced rate of increase in output voltage indicates that the amplifier output is being overdriven and the output waveform distorted. Now, reduce the level of the amplifier's input (the audio oscillator's output) to a convenient value — about one half the level that caused clipping of the output voltage.

● Frequency Response

The frequency response of the tape recorder's audio amplifier can be measured with the same test circuit of *Figure 6-15*. A typical frequency response curve (or graph) is shown in *Figure 6-16*. Note that the frequency response cannot be checked accurately unless the tone controls are first set to mid-range. To measure the output signal from the amplifier you should use the scale on the voltmeter calibrated in decibels. Use an input signal level V_{in}, measured with the meter as shown, that is below the one-half level so the output waveform will not be clipped. Change the range on the meter reading the output level so that it reads near mid range.

Set the frequency of the audio oscillator to 1,000 cycles per second (Hertz). Using the voltmeter measuring V_{output}, adjust the volume control until the meter reads 0 db on the decibel scale. Both meters measuring V_{input} and V_{output} must be meters that have a frequency response of their own of up to 20,000 Hertz. Do not change the volume control or tone control settings.

Figure 6-15. Circuit Arrangement for Measurement of Freqency Response

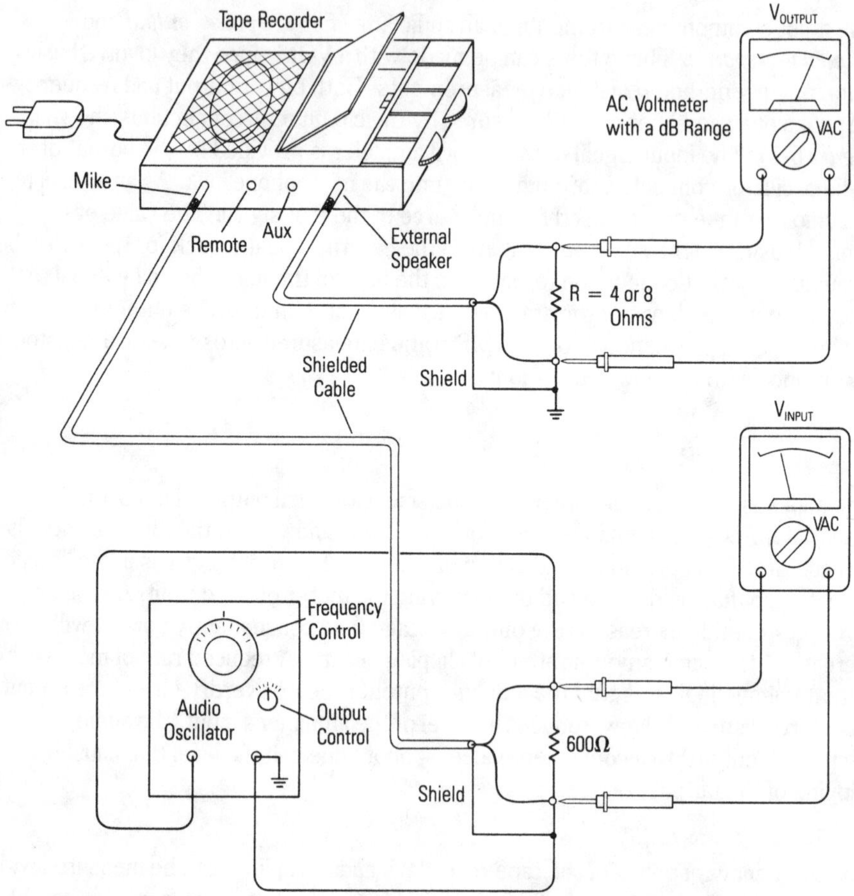

Change the frequency of the oscillator to 2,000 Hertz. Make sure V_{input} is constant and measure V_{output} on the decibel scale. Plot the result on a frequency response plot shown in *Figure 6-16*. For 2,000 Hertz the reading in *Figure 6-16* is still 0 db.

Increase the frequency of the oscillator in 2,000 Hertz steps, measuring V_{input} to make sure it remains constant at each step, and plot V_{output} in decibels at each step on the frequency response of *Figure 6-16*. Most audio systems have good response (within 3 db) at least to 15,000 Hertz. Measurements can be made up to 100,000 Hertz if the meters have frequency responses to respond to such a high frequency.

After the frequency response above 1,000 cycles has been measured, reduce the oscillator frequency in 100 or 50 Hertz steps from 1,000 Hertz and measure V_{output} at each step (on the decibel scale) until the frequency is 10 Hertz. A typical response should look like *Figure 6-16*. The measurements and initial calibration point was

Figure 6-16. Typical Frequency Response of a Tape Recorder/Player

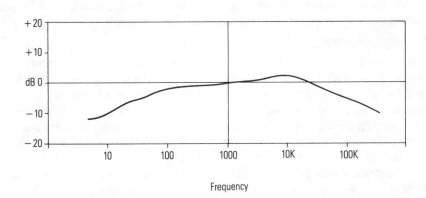

Frequency

started at 1,000 Hertz because that point is usually always within the flat frequency response of any audio system. To say that an amplifier has a "flat" frequency response means that all frequencies are amplified with equal emphasis and the frequency response curve would be ideally, a horizontal line.

If one wants to determine the effect of tone controls, the frequency response measurements can be repeated with the tone controls set at the two extremes.

Troubleshooting the Amplifier

The amplifier in the cassette recorder/player is a semiconductor amplifier. It may be built of discrete components or it may be one or two integrated circuits. If it is a completely contained integrated circuit, it will be difficult to troubleshoot for a problem unless a circuit schematic is obtained from the manufacturer. However, if it is a discrete component amplifier, then the same techniques described in the previous chapters for transistor amplifiers can be used.

AUTOMOTIVE CIRCUITS

Beneath the hood of your automobile is a remarkable electrical system. This system performs several functions. It produces electrical energy, stores it, and delivers it either at low voltage, sometimes as very high current, or in high voltage surges of up to 35,000 volts. These surges occur at a rate of about 12,000 each mile and at an accuracy of about one ten-thousandth of a second. This electrical system makes your modern motorcar possible. It allows the hand crank to be replaced by the starter motor, supplies electric power for lights, which would have to be gas lanterns otherwise, and the ever increasing number of accessories like the stereo, climate control, and power windows, antenna, and door locks. A very basic, automobile electrical system was shown in *Figure 3-3*. It showed the major components of the system for starting the engine, and the electrical connections between them. The car frame was used as the return circuit; therefore, requiring only half as much wiring.

The car frame, when used like this, is called the electrical ground (a common connection). The battery is the heart of the system and batteries produce only dc; therefore, the automotive electrical system is a direct-current system. The voltages and currents are measured with dc voltmeters and ammeters.

The Charging System

As stated, the automobile electrical system is dc. The alternator (ac generator), however, produces alternating current in its stator winding which is changed to direct current by diodes. To provide a smooth flow of current, automotive alternators are three-phase; that is they are built with three stator windings (coils) which, in effect, give overlapping pulsing of alternating current. Most automotive alternators use the Y-connected stator circuit as shown in *Figure 6-17*. When these pulses are rectified by the six-diode bridge, a comparatively smooth direct current is obtained. The stator windings can remain permanently connected to the battery because the diodes in the stator-to-battery circuit prevent the battery from discharging through the stator windings when the engine is not running.

When a battery is low, it will accept a lot of current, but when it is fully charged, it will take only a very small current. When an alternator is attempting to charge a battery that is fully charged, its output voltage continues to increase in order to get current through the battery. If this alternator output voltage were allowed to continually increase, the battery would be overcharged and thus ruined. The voltage regulator guards against excessively high alternator output voltage.

Electrical Checks on the Alternator

A simple check of the alternator can be made by connecting a voltmeter across the battery terminals and then starting the car. There should be three distinct readings: First, the battery voltage before starting should be about 12.6 volts. Then, while starting, it should drop to no less than 10 volts. After starting the voltage across the battery should rise to near 14 volts if the alternator is charging it. If the alternator is not charging the battery several simple checks can be made to check it.

The field coil can be "quick-checked" by bringing a screwdriver blade against the back of the alternator, in the center, and check the magnetic field strength difference with the engine off, and then running. If the field is significantly stronger with the alternator turning, the field coil is functioning properly, if not, there is no current through the field coil.

There are only three parts to check if an alternator fails to produce any output: the stator, the rotor windings and circuit, and the diodes and circuit. These are tests to be made with the alternator on the bench.

1. Testing the Rotor Field Coil: A good check of the field coil is a "current draw" test. Use your VOM/DVM as an ammeter on its high current range and connect it between the F terminal and the battery. Slowly turn the rotor by hand. The field coil current should be about 2.5 amps at 12 volts applied. A low current draw indicates high resistance in the field circuit. This may be due to brushes not seating well on the slip rings, dirty or worn slip rings, or poor connections in the field coils. Excessive current drawn indicates a possible shorted field coil or a

Figure 6-17. Wiring Diagram of an Alternator and Regulator

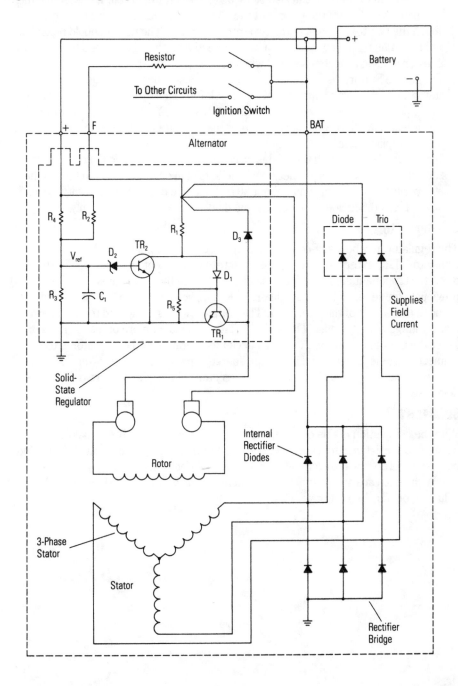

grounded field circuit.

   An ohmmeter check can also be made of the rotor field coil. Disassemble the alternator to separate the rotor. Set the ohmmeter to Rx1 and zero the meter. Touch the two test probes to the two rotor slip rings. The meter should read about 4 ohms. A high reading indicates a bad connection at the slip ring or a broken wire. A lower reading indicates shorted windings.

2. Testing the Stator: disassemble the alternator, disconnect the diodes from the stator leads and, with your ohmmeter, check for a short from each lead to the stator pole frame, then check for continuity from the Y connection to all three stator leads. A short or an open on either test indicates that the stator will require replacement.

3. Testing the Diodes: with the diodes disconnected as above, and the ohmmeter zeroed on the Rx10 range, check each diode first in one direction and then in the other. Diodes should measure about 50 ohms in one direction and infinity in the other. If any diode does not, replace the diode or the rectifier assembly.

The Regulator

The regulator may be a self-contained integrated circuit amplifier with a power transistor, TR_1, external, or it may be a discrete component amplifier. If it is a discrete component amplifier, it can be checked using the techniques described previously for semiconductor amplifiers. TR_1 supplies current to the rotor (field) to regulate the output of the alternator. The voltage, V_{ref}, is compared to the zener diode voltage of D_2 to cause TR_1, through TR_2, to conduct more or less to raise or lower the alternator output. A way to check the operation of the regulator is to connect the + lead to a variable voltage source separate from the battery. As the voltage at the + terminal is varied, the alternator voltage should increase or decrease.

SUMMARY

With the completion of this chapter, the reader should now be able to make voltage, current and resistance measurements with a VOM or DVM in any kind of circuit and be able to determine if the circuit components are operating properly.

   With good care and careful measurements, your VOM or DVM will prove to be a valuable tool for the rest of your life.

GLOSSARY

Alternating current (ac): An electrical current that periodically changes in magnitude and in direction of the current.

Alternation: Either half of a cycle of alternating current. It is the time period during which the current increases from zero to its maximum value (in either direction) and decreases to zero.

Alternator (or ac generator): An electromechanical device which transforms mechanical energy into electrical energy — an alternating current. Very early users called this a dynamo.

Ammeter: An instrument for measuring ac or dc electrical current in a circuit. Unless magnetically coupled, it must be placed in the current path so the flow is through the meter.

Ammeter shunt: A low-resistance conductor that is used to increase the range of an ammeter. It is shunted (placed in parallel) across the ammeter movement and carries the majority of the current.

Ampere (A): The unit of measurement for electrical current in coulombs (6.25×10^{18} electrons) per second. One ampere results in a circuit that has one ohm resistance when one volt is applied to the circuit. See Ohm's law.

Amplification: See Gain.

Amplifier: An electrical circuit designed to increase the current, voltage, or power of an applied signal.

Analog-to-Digital Conversion or Converter (ADC or A/D): The process of converting a sampled analog signal to a digital code that represents the amplitude of the original signal sample.

Audio and audio frequency (AF): The range of frequencies normally heard by the human ear. Typically, about 20 to 20,000 Hz.

Beta (β): The current gain of a transistor when connected in a common emitter circuit.

Bias: In an electronic circuit, a voltage or current applied to an active device (transistor, diode, etc.) to set the steady-state operating point of the circuit.

Binary Coded Decimal (BCD): A binary numbering system in which any decimal digit is represented by a group of 4 bits. Each digit in a multi-digit number continues to be identified by its 4-bit group.

Binary digit (Bit): A digit in the binary number system whose value can be either 1 or 0.

Bipolar: A semiconductor device having both majority and minority carriers.

Bit: See Binary digit.

Block diagram: A system diagram which shows the relationship between the main functional units of the system represented by blocks.

Breakdown: The condition for a reverse-biased semiconductor junction when its high resistance, under the reverse bias, suddenly decreases, causing excessive current. Not necessarily destructive.

Bridge rectifier: A full-wave rectifier in which the rectifier diodes are connected in a bridge circuit to allow current to the load during both the positive and negative alternation of the supply voltage.

Capacitance (C): The capability to store charge in an electrostatic field. It can be expressed as equal to the charge Q in coulombs that is stored divided by the voltage E in volts that supplied the charge. Capacitance tends to oppose any change in voltage. The unit is farads.

Capacitive reactance (Xc): The opposition that a capacitor offers to a time changing signal or supplied voltage. Its value is $X_c = \dfrac{1}{2\pi fc}$

Capacitor (C): A device made up of two metallic plates separated by a dielectric or insulating material. Used to store electrical energy in the electostatic field between the plates.

Cathode (K): The negative electrode of a semiconductor diode.

Charge (Q): A measurable quantity of electrical energy representing the electrostatic forces between atomic particles. Electrons have a negative charge.

Choke: An inductance which is designed to pass large amounts of dc current. It usually is used in power supply filters to help reduce ripple; although, there are inductances called rf chokes (rfc) which prevent rf from feeding to a circuit.

Circuit: A complete path that allows electrical current from one terminal of a voltage source to the other terminal.

Circuit breaker: An electromagnetic switch used as a protective device. It breaks a circuit if the current exceeds a specified value.

Clock or Clock generator: An electronic circuit that generates accurate and precisely controlled, regularly occurring, synchronizing or timing signals called clock signals.

Clock rate: The frequency of oscillation of the master clock, or oscillator, in a system.

Coil: The component that is formed when several turns of wire are wound on a cylindrical form or on a metal core.

Collector (C): The element in a transistor that collects the moving electrons or holes, and from which the output usually is obtained. Analogous to the plate of a triode vacuum tube.

Color code: A system in which colors are used to identify the value of electronic components, or other variables, such as component tolerance.

Component: The individual parts that make up a circuit, a function, a subsystem or a total piece of equipment.

Conductor: A substance through which electrons flow with relative ease.

Contactor: A special relay for switching heavy currents at power line voltages.

Continuity: A continuous electrical path.

Controlled rectifier: A four-layer semiconductor device in which conduction is triggered ON by gate current and OFF by reducing the anode voltage below a critical value.

Coulomb (C): The unit of electrical charge, made up of a quantity of 6.25×10^{18} electrons.

Current (I): The flow of electrons, measured in amperes. One ampere results when one volt is impressed on a circuit that has a resistance of one ohm.

Decibel (db): The standard unit for expressing the ratio between powers P_1 and P_2. db $= 10\log_{10}P_1/P_2$, one tenth of a bel.

Dielectric: The non-conducting material used to separate the plates of a capacitor or for insulating electric contacts.

Digital signal: A signal whose level has only discrete values, like on or off, 1 or 0, +5v or +0.2v.

Digital to Analog Conversion (or Converter) (DAC or D/A): A circuit that accepts digital input signals and converts them to an analog output signal.

Diode: A device which has two terminals and has a high resistance to current in one direction and a low resistance to current in the other direction.

Direct Current (DC, dc): Current in a circuit in one direction only.

Drain: The element in field-effect transistor which is roughly analagous to the collector of a bipolar transistor.

Effective value: The value of ac current that will produce the same heating effect in a load resistor as the corresponding value of dc current.

Electricity: A form of energy produced by the flow of electrons through materials and devices under the influence of an electromotive force produced electrostatically, mechanically, chemically or thermally.

Electrolytic capacitor: A capacitor whose electrodes are immersed in a wet electrolyte or dry paste.

Electromotive force (E): The force which causes an electrical current in a circuit when there is a difference in potential. Synonym for voltage.

Electron: The basic atomic particle having a negative charge that rotates around a positively charged nucleus of an atom.

Electrostatic field: The electrical field or force surrounding objects that have an electrical charge.

Emitter (E): The semiconductor material in a transistor that emits carriers into the base region when the emitter-base junction is forward biased.

Error: Any deviation of a computed, measured, or observed value from the correct value.

Farad (F): The basic unit for capacitance. A capacitor has a value of one farad when it has stored one coulomb of charge with one volt across it.

Field coil: An electromagnet formed from a coil of insulated wire wound around a soft iron core. Commonly used in motors and generators.

Field-Effect Transistor (FET): A 3-terminal semiconductor device where current is from source to drain due to a conducting channel formed by a voltage field between the gate and the source.

Filament: The heated element in an incandescent lamp or vacuum tube.

Filter: A circuit element or group of components which passes signals of certain frequencies while blocking signals of other frequencies.

Fluorescent: The ability to emit light when struck by electrons or other radiation.

Forward resistance: The resistance of a forward-biased junction when there is current through the semiconductor p-n junction.

Forward voltage (or bias): A voltage applied across a semiconductor junction in order to permit forward current through the junction and the device.

Frequency (F or f): The number of complete cycles of a periodic waveform during one second.

Gain (G): 1. Any increase in the current, voltage or power level of a signal. 2. The ratio of output to input signal level of an amplifier.

Ground (or Grounded): 1. The common return path for electric current in electronic equipment. Called electrical ground. 2. A reference point connected to or assumed to be at zero potential with respect to the earth.

Henry (H or h): The unit of inductance. The inductance of a coil of wire in henries is a function of the coils size, the number of turns of wire and the type core material.

Hertz (Hz): One cycle per second.

Impedance (Z): In a circuit, the opposition that circuit elements present alternating current. The impedance includes both resistance and reactance.

Inductance (L): The capability of a coil to store energy in a magnetic field surrounding it which results in a property that tends to oppose any change in the existing current in the coil.

Inductive reactance (X_L): The opposition that an inductance offers when there is an ac or pulsating dc in a circuit. $X_L = 2\pi fL$.

Input impedance: The impedance seen by a source when a device or circuit is connected across the source.

Integrated circuit (IC): A complex semiconductor structure that contains all the circuit components for a high functional density analog or digital circuit interconnected together on a single chip of silicon.

Junction: The region separating two layers in a semiconductor material, e.g. a p-n junction.

Junction transistor: A PNP or NPN transistor formed from three alternate regions of p an n type material. The alternate materials are formed by diffusion or ion implantation.

Leakage (or Leakage current): The undesired flow of electricity around or through a device or circuit. In the case of semiconductors, it is the current across a reverse biased semiconductor junction.

Linear amplifier: A class A amplifier whose output signal is directly proportional to the input signal. The output is an exact reproduction of the input except for the increased gain.

Load: Any component, circuit, subsystem or system that consumes power delivered to it by a source of power.

Loop: A closed path around which there is a current or signal.

Magnetic Field: The force field surrounding a magnet.

Magnetic lines of force: The imaginary lines called flux lines used to indicate the directions of the magnetic forces in a magnetic field.

Megohm (MΩ): A million ohms. Sometimes abbreviated meg.

Microampere (μA): One millionth of an ampere.

Microfarad (μfd, MFD, or mfd): One millionth of a farad.

Milliampere (mA): One thousandth of an ampere.

Millihenry (mH): One thousandth of a henry.

Milliwatt (mW): One thousandth of a watt.

NPN Transistor: A bipolar transistor with a p-type base sandwiched between an n-type emitter, and an n-type collector.

N-type semiconductor material (N): A semiconductor material in which the majority carriers are electrons, and there is an excess of electrons over holes.

Ohm (Ω): The unit of electrical resistance. A circuit component has a resistance of one ohm when one volt applied to the component produces a current of one ampere.

Ohms-per-volt: The sensitivity rating for a voltmeter. Also expresses the impedance (resistance) presented to a circuit by the meter when a voltage measurement is made.

Open circuit: An incomplete path for current.

Operating point: The steady state or no signal operating point of a circuit or active device.

Operational amplifier (OP AMP): A high-gain analog amplifier with two inputs and one output.

Oscillation: A sustained condition of continuous operation where the circuit outputs a constant signal at a frequency determined by circuit constants and as a result of positive or regenerative feedback.

Pi (π): The mathematical constant which is equal to the ratio of the circumference of a circle to its diameter. Approximately 3.14.

Picofarad (pf): A unit of capacitance that is 1×10^{-12} farads or one millionth of a millionth of a farad.

Piezoelectric: A crystal property which causes a voltage to be developed across the crystal when mechanical stress is applied, or vice-versa.

PNP Transistor: A bipolar transistor with an n-type base sandwiched between a p-type emitter and a p-type collector.

Polarity: The description of whether a voltage is positive or negative with respect to some reference point.

Potential difference: The voltage difference between two points, calculated algebraically.

Power (P): The time rate of doing work.

Power (reactive): The product of the voltage and current in a reactive circuit measured in volt-amperes (apparent power).

Power (real): The power dissipated in the purely resistive components of a circuit measured in watts.

Power supply: A defined unit that is the source of electrical power for a device, circuit, subsystem or system.

P-type semiconductor material (P): A semiconductor material in which holes are the majortiy carriers and there is a deficiency of electrons.

Reactance (X): The opposition that a pure inductance or a pure capacitance provides to current in an ac circuit.

Rectification: The process of converting alternating current into pulsating direct current.

Relay: A device in which a set of contacts is opened or closed by a mechanical force supplied by turning on current in an electromagnet. The contacts are isolated from the electromagnet.

Resistance (R): A characteristic of a material that opposes the flow of electrons. It results in loss of energy in a circuit dissipated as heat.

Resistor (R): A circuit component that provides resistance to current in the circuit.

Reverse current: The current when a semiconductor junction is reverse biased.

Root-Mean-Square (RMS): See effective value. The RMS value of an ac sinusoidal waveform is 0.707 of the peak amplitude of the sine wave.

Semiconductor: One of the materials falling between metals as good conductors and insulators as poor conductors in the periodic chart of the elements.

Shunt: A parallel circuit branch, see Ammeter shunt.

Signal: In electronics, the information contained in electrical quantities of voltage or current that forms the input, timing, or output of a device, circuit, or system.

Silicon Controlled Rectifier (SCR): A semiconductor diode in which current through a third element, called the gate, controls turn-on, and the anode-to-cathode voltage controls turn-off.

Sine (sinusoidal) wave: A waveform whose amplitude at any time through a rotation of an angle from 0° to 360° is a function of the sine of an angle.

Step-down transformer: A transformer in which the secondary winding has fewer turns than the primary.

Step-up transformer: A transformer in which the secondary winding has more turns than the primary.

Transformer: A set of coils wound on an iron core in which a magnetic field couples energy between two or more coils or windings.

Transistor: A three-terminal semiconductor device used in circuits to amplify electrical signals or to perform as a switch to provide digital functions.

Turns ratio: The ratio of secondary winding turns to primary winding turns of a transformer.

Vector: A line representing the magnitude and time phase of some quantity, plotted on rectangular or polar coordinates.

Voltage (or Volt): The unit of electromotive force that causes current when included in a closed circuit. One volt causes a current of one ampere through a resistance of one ohm.

Voltage drop: The difference in potential between two points caused by a current through an impedance or resistance.

Watt (W): The unit of electrical power in joules per second, equal to the voltage drop (in volts) times the current (in amperes) in a resistive circuit.

INDEX